CONSCIENCE HILL

Reflections by Ralph Needham

First Published in 2011 by TUCANN*books*

ISBN 978-1-907516-14-6

Text © Ralph Needham 2011
Design © TUCANN*books* 2011

Produced by: TUCANNdesign&print, 19 High Street, Heighington, Lincoln LN4 1RG
Tel & Fax: 01522 790009
Website. www.tucann.co.uk

**To my wife Pat
for her patience and understanding
whilst I have worked on the text
and her invaluable work editing the manuscript**

"Age is a question of mind over matter.
If you don't mind it doesn't matter"

Mark Twain

INDEX

CHAPTER 1
Reflections

It's a little after 5'o clock on a sunny afternoon in early September as I pull my tractor to a halt on the summit of Conscience Hill and commence a short break from cultivating the surrounding field in preparation for its next crop. The noise of the powerful engine drops away to a gentle tick over as I pour a cup of tea from my flask and sit back in the tractor seat to enjoy a meal of tasty sandwiches that my wife Pat has prepared for me.

It's at times like this that I nostalgically reflect on the many changes that I have been lucky enough to observe as I gaze over the surrounding countryside from this relatively high point.

If you pick up an Ordnance Survey Explorer Series, Sheet 283 of north east Lincolnshire scaled at 2.1/2 inches to the mile you will notice the name Conscience Hill situated midway between Louth and the village of South Cockerington.

The hill is encircled by the 20 meters, (65 feet) contour, though the actual summit of the hill is almost 25 meters (80 feet) above sea level.

In the general scheme of things Conscience Hill doesn't represent a very large hill, - probably little more than a hump when compared to the wolds which rise to more than 120 meters only three miles to the west, but with its commanding views overlooking the flat land between the Lincolnshire Wolds and the sea the hill seems almost like a mountain from my position up here.

As the glaciers that made up the ice sheet covering this part of eastern England 10,000 years ago melted. Conscience Hill was formed by debris carried within the glacier to leave the moraine we see today.

It's a testament to the power of the glacier when one considers that perhaps the ten million tons of material that makes up Conscience Hill was suspended within the ice as the glacier bulldozed its way south.

There is no rock or stone on the surface, in spite of one large rock been recovered during an archaeological dig during the 1920s when it was moved down to Hall Farm. It's quite noticeable that the soil on both the eastern and western side of the hill is very friable and easily worked, whilst the soils to the north and particularly the south of the summit contains a high proportion of clay making them particularly difficult to cultivate.

Conscience Hill has always held a particular fascination for me resulting in my enjoying working up here more than on any other field on the farm.

Certainly it's the only field where I can see any great distance as so much of the farm in common with the rest of the Marsh is completely flat with much of the eastern part being little more than 2 to 3 meters above sea level.

I believe that there is something almost mystical about being up here that induces a feeling of detachment from everyday life because the nearest houses and buildings lie a considerable distance away from its remote elevated position. They appear little changed, to how I remember them looking 65 years ago, in spite of the fact that field boundaries have changed significantly and cropping patterns are completely different.

I recall so many unique village characters now deceased, who lived within sight of Conscience Hill. I remember how they went about their everyday lives practising skills that future generation can only read about in history books.

Jack Patrick was a highways road lengths man, whilst his wife ran the small post office from their house at Pub corner. Even though many years have passed since they lived there, the house from this distance still looks remarkably similar to how I remember it looking when I used to pass it on my daily way to North Cockerington Primary School in the 1940s.

At the next corner closer to the village of South Cockerington, I remember Arthur and Margaret Humberstone's smallholding. Their mud and stud, house with its red painted tin roof was situated tight on the corner. An assorted range of small wooden farm buildings for his farm animals lay beyond the house and garden.

In addition to running his smallholding Arthur was sexton at St Leonards whilst his wife Margaret cleaned the church and provided a constant supply of altar flowers from her garden.

As my gaze shifts to the south I can see the full length of Stewton Road. With a little effort I can visualize Bob Parker Cycling up the road with his trusty twelve bore strapped to the crossbar of his bike. He generally wore a battered trilby hat, rolled down thigh boots and voluminous coat with its multitude of pockets capable of holding anything from a pigeon to a cauliflower.

As I shift my gaze to the western end of the lane I have to use a little

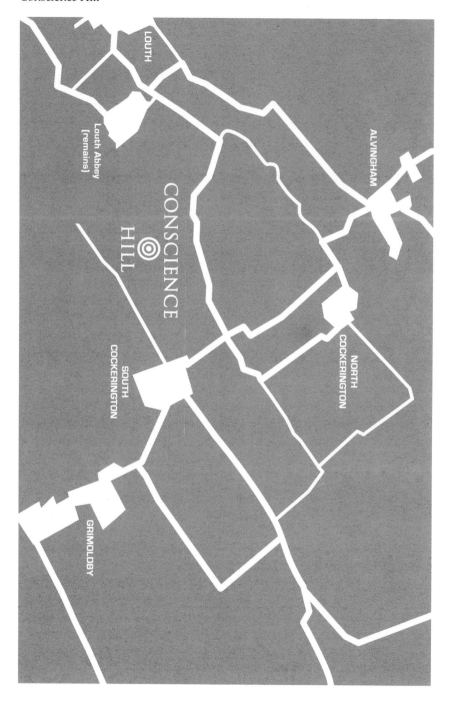

Looking west from Conscience Hill towards Louth Park Abbey and Louth.

more imagination to recall where Bill and George Hoyes once lived with their two spinster sisters as there is now little left to give any indication that a farming family once lived and earned their living there. The farm house has long since disappeared to become part of an arable field with only one farm building still remaining as a final memorial to their lifetimes work spent farming.

I am reminded of men like Arthur Benton who could be reliably contacted in an evening at the Prussian Queen, in Saltfleetby when it was possible to make arrangements for him to butcher a pig during the winter months or come with two of his colleague's sheep shearing during the early summer.

I remember Arthur and Walt West and their joiners shop down Chapel lane and how they could turn their hands to anything from constructing buildings or farm trailers to making coffins for a funeral.

A little further down the same lane was the village shop that despite its tiny size was a veritable Aladdin's cave stocking items as varied as paraffin to pilchards and bootlaces to bovril.

And then of course there were the farms and the characters who worked on them. Sixty years later almost all those farms are amalgamated into much larger units.

There were so many unique individuals; men like Foggy Green who used to graze his father's cattle on the roadside verges leading into Louth and Harry Smith, the chimney sweep, in his three wheeled Reliant van, to name but two.

Whilst I am in this nostalgic frame of mind I start to speculate on people in earlier centuries who have surveyed the district from this vantage point.

I think about the Vavasours and the Scropes who lived in the Hall only a short distance from where I now live and their connection with Louth Park Abbey in the 14th Century. Yet as I gaze over the next couple of fields to the west, I can just detect the last crumbling chalk remains of the Abbey. The enormous edifice would have completely dominated the fourteenth to seventeenth century skyline but has now almost disappeared from the landscape, as the final remains melt slowly into the surrounding grass field revealing no hint of the violence and intrigue of that troubled period.

I speculate on the relationship between Abbot Walter of Louth and Sir Henry le Vavasour from South Cockerington and wonder what hold the Abbot held over him, particularly when it came to offering him divine redemption by interring him under the grand altar. What intrigue involving bribery and corruption would have been enacted within sight of Conscience Hill to build the great Abbey?

Where did the master builder come from whose life time's work would have been employed in designing and building the magnificent cathedral like building?

And what about the small army of masons and labourers who carried out the construction? Where did they and their families live, and how were they paid? So many unanswered questions regarding what today would be regarded as a major building project but is now almost lost from sight as though it had never existed.

And then my thoughts drift to the origin on the very name Conscience Hill. How did it get its unusual name? Was it once the site of a pagan ritual, or maybe even a place where pre Christian worship was carried out? Or could this lonely elevated spot have been a place where Monks from the nearby Abbey gave penitence for misdeeds real or imagined?

On the other hand perhaps someone was murdered here or might it have been a burial spot for Black Death bodies from successive plagues? An observer on this hill in 1349 would certainly have experienced the Black Death with all its horrors, followed by the sixteenth century plagues in all their forms, resulting in the abandonment of plague villages such as North Cockerington and their relocation onto clean ground.

Conscience Hill rock, very similar to the bluestone rock in Louth museum.

Flint tool found near the summit of C H.

The ransacking of the Abbey by Henry VlII, leading to the Lincolnshire rising in 1536, must have filled the men, who were grazing stock or cultivating the land for crops here with alarm and made them wonder just what was going to happen next.

Farming however must have been practiced on this ground from the very earliest of times when the production of wool was exported to the "low countries" from ports such as Saltfleet five miles or so to the east. It was the sale of wool that gave rise to the prosperity of the area, as evident by the fine churches and the Abbey itself.

A few years ago I picked up a small flint tool only yards away from where I am now sitting that had clearly been used for skinning animals or cutting meat. The sides of the stone had been carefully shaped to provide a comfortable position for the thumb and index finger, leading down to a half inch wide sharpened blade at the end.

It's at times like this, sitting in an air conditioned cab, that I speculate on the quality of life of the Stone Age man who had fashioned the tool and wonder under what circumstances it had been lost here. Did he live here on this elevated vantage point, to perhaps give him and other members of his community early warning of attack by marauding raiders, or could it simply be that this was one of the drier parts of the surrounding marsh area?

Conscience Hill and farming are inextricably linked and reflect the changing fortunes through the ages. I recollect on the trials and tribulations that my father endured in maintaining a constant supply of water for stock to drink from the flow of water in Monks Dyke that travels around three sides of the field. The water originated from a spring in Louth and then at a point on the west side of Conscience Hill was precisely divided by means of a weir so that equal amounts went to both North and South Cockerington. At certain times in the summer unscrupulous individuals would dig away the bank at the weir allowing the majority of the water to flow to North Cockerington, with consequential dire consequences in denying our stock a constant supply of water that they relied on to drink.

The air quality is now crystal clear as a strengthening north westerly breeze gives the first hint of the colder weather that lays in wait as autumn gives way to winter, but for now the excellent clarity ensures I have a commanding view over the long field enabling me to see a panoramic view all around me.

Conscience Hill looking east towards the coast.

The Lincolnshire Wolds that are little more than three miles away at their nearest point, completely dominate the western skyline as they extend both to the north and south going pretty well as far as the eye can see. The silhouettes of isolated clumps of trees in the foreground merge into a series of much larger woods at Muckton, Haugham, Cawthorpe and Burwell to form a near continuous line of trees stretching far away to the south.

I can see snail like lorries and cars climbing the incline from Louth up to Kenwick Top on the A16 as they make their way south towards Boston, whilst beyond the town sticking up rather like a 1,200 foot pencil, the Belmont television mast seems to be an almost alien like intrusion as its height dominates the Wold Vista. Slightly to its left at Stenigot I can see the preserved wooden latticed Second World War radar mast, which was one of four erected there to play such a pivotal part in the U.K. air defence system during the Second World War. The sight of the Stenigot radar mast triggers a multitude of memories as I remember all manner of childhood experiences growing up during the Second World War.

Nestling on the eastern edge of the Wolds lays the market town of Louth less than a couple of miles away, commanded by the graceful 300 foot spire of St. James Church. Houses and streets, particularly at the southern end of the town can be seen clawing their way up the side of the valley through which the river Lud flows and from which Louth's former name of Luda was given to the original settlement. The towering white concrete Malt Kiln looking rather like the great keep of an enormous medieval castle jars the senses as it stands like a lonely sentinel at the top of Newbridge Hill looking over the nearby industrial area of the town.

Further to the right the now disused, chalk quarry at North Ormsby, was once a valuable source of lime for correcting acidity on the marsh fields and is still clearly visible as a white scar set into the eastern Wolds hillside surrounded by a sea of sienna coloured stubble fields.

A plume of white smoke from the giant Tioxide factory chimney 18 miles away on the south bank of the Humber makes the only blotch in an otherwise clear blue sky. The factory now uses lime from the vast quarries at Melton Ross in the north of the county for the production of paint pigments.

Looking east the panorama of patchwork fields and villages, interspersed with isolated farms, stretches away to the coast six miles away. My eye is drawn to the spire of South Somercotes church, known as "Queen of the Marsh", and its long connection with the Needham family. To its right I can clearly see the isolated Skidbroke Church standing like some beached medieval ship marooned in the middle of an arable field a mile from the coastal village of Saltfleet. Beyond, over the out marsh, land and sea seem to merge into a kaleidoscope of differing shades of mauves and pale blues making it difficult to differentiate between where the land ends and the sea begins.

A couple of miles to the south I can see the five great aircraft hangers that act as a constant reminder that Manby was a vital training base for the RAF until its closure in 1972, whilst about a mile away to the east surrounded by deciduous trees, whose leaves are now starting to give way to their autumnal colours, I can see the rectangular Norman church tower of St Leonard in the village of South Cockerington where I grew up and still live.

Sixty Five years ago when I first recall coming to this spot as a child, fields looked quite different with the vista then having a much greater proportion of grass fields grazing livestock, compared to the preponderence of arable fields today. In the interests of maximising food production after the Second World War, grants were paid for fields to be under drained and amalgamated by the removal of hedges so that larger machinery could be used.

If I close my eyes I can visualize many of the local farmers from over half a century ago. Les Street had a herd of black and white Fresian cows at Keddington corner. I remember his portly frame and ruddy complexion with an unlit cigarette seemingly permanently attached to the upper lip of his round face topped by a flat cap. His droll sense of humour wasn't always appreciated by some of the townsfolk, who regularly exercised their dogs in his grass field by the Louth canal, as he had a pathological hatred of unleashed dogs disturbing his cows.

Moving along the Louth road to the north of me, I would easily have seen the Channel Island cattle belonging to the three small dairy farms of Messrs Green, Kent and Hallgarth. To the south Bill and George Hoyes herd of Lincoln Red cattle and flock of cross bred sheep grazed the fields on either side of Stewton Lane. A thick overgrown hawthorn hedge part of the way up the eastern slope of Conscience Hill used to divide the bottom 26 acres from the western 30 acres that encompassed the hills summit. Until the early 1970s when the amalgamated field was under drained, the 26 acres were grazed by our yearling Lincoln Red heifers during the summer, followed by 'in lamb' ewes from our commercial sheep flock during the winter.

Looking further east towards the coast I remember that the fields of grazing cattle and sheep tended to merge into either dull red or smoky grey blobs silhouetted against the green grass.

Sat here today I have a commanding view of the road leading from the coast as it passes through South Cockerington on its way to Louth. My first view of vehicles approaching from the east commences just after they leave South Somercotes village more than 5 miles away, when my position enables me to keep them in view for most of the time until they reach Keddington corner 7 or 8 minutes later. For the first 2 miles up to Hedgends, the road is bordered by deep ditches when the road surface is little more than 2 metres above sea level as it passes a couple of isolated farms at Scupholme, before skirting the deceptively dangerous Brickpits bend and then continues in a westerly direction. The highway then passes through a slight chicane at Hedgends where the ditches of the marsh give way to roadside hedges as the road starts to elevate from about 3 meters above sea level, until it reaches a height of 10 meters some 2 miles later at New Corner in South Cockerington. The road then passes around a series of bends in the village before turning on to Louth road at Pub corner as it covers the next 1½ miles up to Keddington corner where I eventually lose sight of it. This thoroughfare now carries a seemingly constant stream of cars throughout the day with peaks during the early morning and evening as people commute to Louth from the surrounding dormitory villages.

15

Fifty years ago the vast majority of villagers either worked on local farms or found employment with village businesses with the result that relatively few travelled to town to find employment, consequently there was little traffic on the road. I would however have seen a multitude of different coloured coaches originating from Conisholme, North Somercotes, Saltfleet and Mablethorpe carrying shoppers into Louth, with extra coaches running on market days to cater for the additional passengers as few folk had cars.

Grayscroft coaches from Mablethorpe frequently had to supplement their regular coach with two extra ones in order to satisfy the demand at peak times. Wrights red coaches were based in Louth and they passed through the village every hour or so as they operated a very lucrative service conveying RAF personnel and their families from the very important RAF base at Manby, to either shop in Louth or catch the London train from the station.

The single fare to Louth at that time was 2½ d, or 1½ d for a child.

At a time before the public utilities, that we take for granted, were connected to the village, people generated their own entertainment within the village community. In 1945 few folk had a radio because it entailed getting a heavy glass accumulator recharged in Louth or any other centre that had electrical power. In any event the recharged accumulators didn't last long as the glass valves in the early radios used a great deal of power. As television was still in its infancy "the pictures" in Louths two cinemas provided escapism whilst Sunday services at the village Church and Chapel were well attended, and people met socially at the Whist Drives held in North Cockerington school.

CHAPTER TWO
How it was

Both sides of my family are steeped in farming history that can be traced back for hundreds of years, so it's little wonder that I've spent my entire life farming. My two grandfathers however, took quite differing approaches in the methods that they adopted in order to start farming, towards the end of the nineteenth century. In both instances although they received knocks, that would have daunted lesser men, they stuck to their last with steadfast courage and perseverance and succeeded in establishing a foothold on the farming ladder. For at least the last 350 years, and probably for much longer, generations of my Needham ancestors have worked in agriculture never living a deal more than 8 miles from Conscience Hill, and for most of the last 200 years within its sight.

My Grandfather Needham, with help from his father started farming in a very modest way on a few acres of rented land in South Cockerington in in the mid 1880s, whilst my Grandfather Smith, the son of a Waggoner at Welton le Wold, decided at about the same time that with little prospects of getting a foot on the farming ladder in this country he would find farm work in America.

The Needham family tree can be traced back in a direct line over 11 generations to Thomas Needham who was born c 1676 followed by 3 generations of his descendents who all lived at Fulstow. It's fair to presume that they all worked as farm labourers, until William Needham, (1790-1860) (my great, great grandfather), started farming in the early 1840s on his own account with a few acres, at South Somercotes. We know from census records that he was working as a farm labourer at Louth Park farm adjacent to the old Abbey, when one of his sons also called William was born in 1822. The 1841 census reveals that son William now aged 19 was working as a farm labourer for a Mr John Hodgson in North Cockerington. However the 1851 census shows that William Senior was now farming 54 acres with the assistance of young William now aged 29, and a labourer. Following his father's death in 1860 the younger William took over the farm. He increased the area farmed to 123 acres of which he owned 46 acres. On the Sunday preceding Saltfleet Fair, which since medieval times was traditionally held on the first Saturday in October, the elder William started a family tradition commencing between 1820 and 1830 that was maintained without a break for over 100 years, when he arranged that the current occupier of the family home should invite as many family members as could attend to an annual gathering.

An extract from the Louth Advertiser in October 1926, reports. -

Last Sunday twenty three descendents of the original William Needham composed the gathering. Until he died, two years ago Mr John Needham, (my grandfather), presided over the gathering, now Mr William Needham (brother) occupies that position, but Mr George Needham (brother) is the host who welcomes brothers, sisters, children , and grand children of the family.

The annual event took the form of a church service in South Somercotes church, whose spire stands proud above the flat lands of the surrounding marsh, followed by a meal at the family home.

My Grandfather John William Needham in South View Farmyard circa 1908 with a foal suckling one of his Lincoln Red cows. Note the stacks of straw and how they were cut with a "cutting knife". Spot the figure of either my father or Uncle Jack partially obscured by the cows head.

Cockerington Daisy my Grandfathers most famous Shire horse selling for £2000 in 1920.

My grandfather John William Needham 1858-1924 was the eldest of 5 sons and 7 daughters born to young William and his wife Mary. Two sons died as infants and two daughters remained spinsters. With a large family to provide for, it was quite apparent that his small farm at South Somercotes would be unable to provide employment for the three sons so he helped John then aged 24 in 1882, to rent a smallholding from the Scrope Estate in South Cockerington in order that he could commence farming in his own right. This all took place at a time of severe economic depression in British agriculture as the effects of the repeal of the Corn Laws hastened the decline of farm gate prices. Many young people from farming stock, including my maternal grandfather Henry Smith, could see little prospect in British agriculture so either found work in the expanding towns or emigrated as he did to North America.

The 18 acres at the Hollies in South Cockerington where John William Needham started farming comprised several small fields leading up to Pub corner on the boundary of North Cockerington, followed a couple of years later by him renting a further 30 acres from the Scrope estate down the track opposite the Stewton road spinney.

From left Mary, Brian (my father), Jack Needham circa 1908 Note the wagon load of straw and the heavy iron wheeled cart, no wonder the horse has its head down.

In South View Farm yard small "rulley" transporting a tumbrel, that held straw for feeding cattle circa 1905.

South View Farm yard. My father riding one of his Lincoln Red bulls circa 1925.

At that time and certainly until the Second World War much of the Lincolnshire Marsh extending from Humberston in the north to beyond Skegness in the south was predominantly permanent grassland. With this in mind it's easy to understand the rationale in 1877 for the railway company to construct a branch line leading off the main Grimsby to London railway line at Louth, to connect through the Marsh villages to provide extensive holding and loading facilities for the thousands of cattle that had to be transported to the rich grazing pastures in the Marsh fields. The special spring and autumn cattle sales that were held at Louth, Alford, Spilsby, Burgh le Marsh and Boston were a direct consequence of cattle going on the marshes in the spring or coming off them in the autumn. My grandfather's introduction to farming on his own, in the early 1880s would have been very typical to that experienced by many thousands of other small farmers in eastern England.

In spite of farmers spending incredibly long hours working extremely hard, frequently under appalling weather conditions, their prospects of making a decent living were pretty poor, as they struggled to make any sort of a return from whatever they grew or reared. Legislation introduced in 1840 allowed low cost produce from the expanding farmlands in North America, Australia and other countries of the British Empire to flood into the country with little or no import duty. The price of food was deliberately kept low in order that manufactured goods pouring from British factories could be sold cheaply all over the world. British farmers with their small farms and unfavourable climatic conditions found it difficult to compete on equal terms with these low cost imports from countries that had the great advantage of scale and climate. This had the effect of undermining the value of everything that they produced, resulting in British farming being pushed firmly into the grip of a severe depression.

Although the prospects for a career in farming looked decidedly poor, John was ambitious and wanted to improve his position, so in order to add value to the animals that he was producing he sold the three cows that his father had given him, to start farming, and reinvested the proceeds in two pedigree Lincoln Red cows that he purchased from a leading local breeder. These animals went on to form the foundation of the Cockerington herd, which over the course of the next 75 years multiplied to more than 600 animals making it the breeds largest herd. In spite of improving his small herd of Lincoln Red cattle he wisely decided that there was much more potential income to be made in breeding pedigree Shire horses. Horses were then the principle method of producing motive power on farms. Every farm had its heavy horses with Shires being the dominant breed. In this part of England they had been specifically developed to provide strength and power for the arable farms of Lincolnshire. During the course of the next few years his wise judgement, in breeding high quality animals, earned him widespread recognition in the pedigree Shire horse society, as one of the country's leading Shire horse breeders.

Sometime towards the end of the 1890s he gave up the Hollies in order that his younger brother William could make his own independent start in farming. Probably with the assistance of his father, John obtained the tenancy of the 130 acres South View Farm in South Cockerington from the Scropes estate in place of Mr Marsh Fox who had moved to the Highfield farm in North Cockerington. The farm at that time comprised 55 acres on the north side of Marsh Lane plus another 73 acres opposite Pub corner that was bordered by Pedlar Lane to the east and Louth Road to the north.

My grandfather's next acquisition was to purchase for £600 the 18 acre Saltbox field in Louth Road, North Cockerington that had originally comprised a series of two to three acre allotments, previously cultivated from the time of the enclosures by smallholders or cottage farmers. In the north east corner, presently occupied by the grandly named Saltbox Hall stood a very small dwelling known as Saltbox. It looked and quite literally was half a house with one room and a back kitchen downstairs, plus two small bedrooms upstairs. Immediately to the east of the house was a wooden fenced crew yard standing in front of an open brick building, where cattle were housed for the duration of the winter. I particularly remember during the severe winter of 1947 that drinking water for the cattle had to be transported along the road to the Saltbox yard by means of an under powered, two wheel drive, standard Fordson tractor towing an extremely heavy, all iron constructed tanker. It must have been an absolute nightmare to tow over heavily compacted snow. It was intended to supplement rainwater collected from the buildings roofs and stored in adjacent large, metal tanks. Water for the tanker was extracted from Monks Dyke and pumped into the tank by means of a hydraulic ram, powered solely by the flow of water flowing down the ditch.

Prior to 1920 when Cockerington Hall was demolished, and the estate dissipated, the majority of the land in Cockerington was owned by the Scrope family. They lived in a grand house that overlooked extravagantly laid out grounds, approached by a wide tree lined drive that swept across parkland, giving magnificent views of the Lincolnshire Wolds in the distance.

During the first two decades of the 20th century the Strawson family were the Estates principle tenants, residing at Hall Farm, and farming a large block of land to the east of the hall.

In 1919 the Scrope Estate decided to dispose of their Cockerington property, and rather than offer the houses and farms to the separate tenants decided to sell everything, en bloc, to a man called Frederic Wilkinson.

Mr Wilkinson, the new landlord, would be described as an asset stripper today, and judging by the tenants who refused to purchase their freeholds or accept new tenancies from him, a pretty ruthless one at that. Immediately following his purchase, he offered the freehold of their properties to the existing tenants, with the threat that, if they declined to purchase, then he would radically change the terms of their tenancies from those that they had previously enjoyed under the Scropes. My grandfather, on agreeing to purchase South View Farm, that he had previously rented from the Scrope estate, said to Wilkinson, "If any of the existing tenants decline to purchase or accept the new tenancy I will be happy to purchase the farms". When Wilkinson offered the freehold of Hill House farm to Mr Nicholson who had previously rented it from the Scropes, he declined to purchase the farm or continue with the tenancy, preferring to purchase the smaller West View farm down South View lane that Mr Tom Wright the tenant had decided not to purchase or continue renting.

So it was that my Grandfather came to own Hill House farm, when in addition to purchasing the house and farm buildings he gained possession of 102 acres of land that included Conscience Hill.

However an inventory drawn up by John Taylors of Louth on April 6th 1920 shows an almost pedantic attitude to scraping the last penny of value on every item including the residual value of farmyard manure. The amount of cake that cattle had consumed, between April 1919 and April 1920, was precisely recorded and reflected in the value of farm yard manure giving a total tenant right of £129. 7 shillings.

Wagon house and sheep fold for lambing at Hill House Farm. Note the posts supporting the granary that carried a separate valuation 1960.

Reading the valuation of Hill House Farm, for monies payable for fixtures at Hill House and farm yard, the mind boggles at the triviality of the listed items.

The following list not only describes items considered to be of value over and above the sale price but also gives an insight into the lack of prosperity at the time.

The inventory commences with a lead pump and stone trough on the site of a long since demolished house at the rear of the farm yard. The cast iron guttering and downspouts on the granary are valued along with the three oak posts that support the granary itself. Though quite how the upper floor of the brick granary was supposed to stand if the buyer declined to purchase the supporting posts seems quite amazing. They valued the most mundane of features, when one considers that they even placed a value on boards on the side of the pigeon loft including a loose ladder and two dozen feral pigeons.

Even the slabs forming the barn floor were valued!

Would the seller I wonder, really have removed the barn floor if my grandfather had refused to pay that part of the inventory?

The whole of the exterior fencing surrounding the crewyard was valued in a figure that included posts, doors and rails forming a bull house, plus gates, cribs and racks and four stone troughs under the shed and a crib in a loose box.

They go on to describe five stone troughs in the south crew yard along with nest boxes and fittings in the adjoining poultry shed.

In the paddock near the house they enumerate an iron trough with two lead heads, plus 173 feet of underground lead piping leading from the iron trough to the water troughs in the crew yards. They list an iron tank and stone trough in the big crew yard, whilst a water tub beside the house had eight yards of blue brick paving to form a pathway to the coalhouse. They valued 23 yards of slabs from the coalhouse to the gate, even though it formed a pathway to the house.

Within Hill House itself they listed a Pevril stove, a tiled hearth and mantle piece, 15 window blinds, rollers and racks, 18 stair rods, and 34 eyes. There was a rail and 14 pegs in the entrance hall, plus two lamp hooks in the front room. 16 bacon hooks in the kitchen ceiling were itemised, along with a cupboard and shelves near the fireplace. In what's described as the pig place was a thermos pan containing 20 gallons, whilst next door were brick and tiled coops. In the farm yard they even itemised the wet straw steddles where two straw stacks had once stood. The grand total of all of the above items amounted to £236 7 pence, to say nothing about the seller digging up the water piping across the paddock if the purchaser declined to accept the valuation, and come to that, how do you value feral pigeons, that are a pest in any event.

Aerial view of Hall Farm and St Leonards church 1952.

As a result of the above purchases my grandfather was able to increase his farm size by 102 acres, adding it to the rest of the land that he had accumulated. Following his purchase of Hill House in 1920, he decided to rent the house to Mr Edward Allwood, (who was a brother of Allwood Brothers' the noted carnation breeders of Haywards Heath), who later moved down to Red Leas Farm in North Cockerington. (A farm that we started to rent from Anglian Water in 1995, subsequently purchasing the freehold 6 years later in 2001 as later chapters will reveal). Mr Allwood had served in the army during the First World War and had just resumed his duties as a director of Jacksons, the corn merchants, who had extensive offices and warehouses situated alongside Louth's Riverhead, where he specialized in buying and selling malting barley to local breweries.

I have often wondered why Hill House Farm was so named as it most certainly does not stand on a hill. In fact it stands on fairly level ground approximately 11metres (36 feet) above sea level facing west on the T junction where Stewton road meets Pedlar Lane. The present two storied brick farmhouse was built during the 1890s by the Scropes as an estate farmhouse, to replace an earlier one that stood at the rear of the farm yard fronting Chapel Lane. Could it be that the name Hill House Farm is a contraction of 'Conscience' Hill Farm?

The Allwoods were responsible for laying out the garden and planting a privet hedge around the circumference of the house as prior to their moving to the house it was quite literally in the corner of a grass field.

In 1921 The Strawson family who purchased the freehold of Hall Farm from Wilkinson decided to sell, so my grandfather negotiated an arrangement with the Public Works Loan Board to buy the farm in its entirety for £16 an acre. This meant that in the space of two years from 1920 -1922 his farming commitment changed from renting 130 acres to owning in excess of 400 acres.

In order to capitalize on his Shire horse business, in which he was pre eminent, amply testified by the many trophies that the family still possess, he entered into an arrangement with a Mr Bland, who travelled their Shire stallions, forming a separate stud horse business titled "Needham and Bland" with he as the principle.

Bearing in mind that the early 1920s were the start of yet another severe agricultural depression, it was little wonder that my grandfather was under a great deal of pressure to keep his business viable having so recently committed himself to the purchase of so much extra land. I feel

26

Binding wheat circa 1920 at South Cockerington.

My father and his brother Jack 1955

sure that the anxiety of his heavy financial commitment almost certainly contributed to his early death, at the age of 66 years, in 1924.

Jack his eldest son was born in 1897 and made his first marital home with his new wife Muriel, in 1922 at Hall Farm House commonly known as Strawsons House, which at that time comprised a two storied building, with additional rooms in the attic.

They later moved to South View Farmhouse following the death of my grandfather. My grandmother, now a widow, and her other son Brian (my father) born in 1901 and daughter Mary moved across to Hill House which Mr and Mrs Allwood had vacated when they moved down to the recently purchased Red Leas farm.

West Field, lying on the western side of the Park, was owned by a man called Mr Clark who had purchased his field, in common with all of the other tenants, from Mr Wilkinson but could only access his field by crossing over the Park.

When Jack and Muriel moved to the South View farmhouse in 1925 Mr Clark rented the Hall Farmhouse and moved in there.

As Mr Clark was a bachelor, he offered accommodation to a married couple, Fred Rowlet and his wife, on the understanding that they could both live there rent free, provided that Mrs Rowlet cooked and cleaned for him.

After a while, Clark became so delighted with the attention that Mrs Rowlet was bestowing on him, that he wanted to extend the terms of her employment on a more permanent basis which led to Mr Clark and Mrs Rowlet hurriedly eloping to Theddlethorpe where they set up home together.

Mr Rowlet, it was said, was devastated at the turn of events and moved to a cottage (now called Field View) that had originally been built with squatters rights, on a wide roadside verge in Marsh Lane, more than a century earlier.

West Field was subsequently purchased and added to the farm at I suspect a very favourable price in view of its restricted access.

The next major acquisition came in 1946/47, when my grandfather's younger brother George, who had been farming in the old family farm down Mill Lane, South Somercotes, decided that he would retire from farming and give up the tenancy, as his son Frederick didn't wish to continue with the tenancy.

The major portion of the farm was owned by Mr. Milligan Manby from Thorganby, who had decided to sell all of the outlying farms from the estate. My father and Uncle Jack must have made quite a shrewd move because they immediately agreed to purchase the 140 acre farm for £5000 when it was offered to them. Within only a matter of months they recovered half of the original cost of the farm by selling for £2500 one of the new farms isolated 18 acre grass fields near Skidbrook Church that could only be accessed by crossing over two other fields.

In 1955 they purchased, by auction, Messrs Sharpleys 175 acre, strong land, farm along with the farmhouse and two cottages at Scupholme for £7000, which had the advantage of almost linking up to the Mill Lane Farm.

On completing his schooldays at Louth Grammar School my father joined his father and elder brother Jack on the farm. He took a keen interest in his father's Shire horses where his talent in showing horses soon received national recognition, culminating in Cockerington Daisy realising £2000 in 1920.

My father worked hard throughout his life from the time that he left school in 1915 until poor health started to take its toll when he was in his mid 60s, culminating in his death at the age of 76 in 1977. As mentioned earlier my grandfather tripled the farms size by not only purchasing their tenanted farm but also acquiring other adjacent farms and land as a direct consequence of the Scrope estate divesting its tenanted property. I suppose it was inevitable that the massive financial commitment that my Grandfather incurred must have weighed heavily on his mind, especially as collapsing farm prices at the conclusion of the First World War must have made him question the wisdom of his purchases. His early death left my father then aged 23 and his brother Jack with the freehold of a 410 acre farm and an enormous debt that at a time of lowering agricultural prices as the agricultural depression deepened would take more than 40 years to clear. Throughout those difficult depressed years of the 1920s and 30s my father and his brother Jack struggled to pay mortgage instalments on the farm, when a great many other farms and businesses were going bankrupt all around them.

Those years proved to be exceptionally difficult ones for farming with many acres reverting back to scrub land.

As tractors started to appear my father and uncle foresaw the reduced demand for working horses and decided that the future of pedigree stock breeding lay in the development of the pedigree Lincoln Red herd that their father had started. My father oft remarked that were it not for the sales of pedigree livestock he didn't think that they would have survived. It was into this environment that my father met Miss Ellen Smith (my mother) from Wellsdale, near Donington on Bain in 1930 when she was 22, marrying her two years later. She was educated at the village school and came home to help her mother in a very busy farmhouse. In her spare time she led quite an active social life playing tennis but there was nothing she enjoyed better than to walk around her Father's grass fields at Wellsdale with a shot gun, and a couple of her beloved Springer spaniels at heel hoping to shoot one of the hundreds of rabbits that were such a plague at that time.

My Mother and Father's wedding in 1933. L-R back Harry Smith (mothers brother), Jack Needham, mother and father, Hilda Needham (father's cousin), Henry Smith my Grandfather (who went to America). Front Grandmother Louise Needham and Grandmother Annie Smith.

Married life commenced at Hill House at a time when money was incredibly tight as all the money that the farm earned had to be ploughed back into the business. Her task was to make sufficient money from rearing and selling oven ready Christmas poultry, along with eggs, and butter that she churned from milk provided by the house cow, to provide enough money to pay for all household expenses.

In 1937 as the storm clouds of the Second World War loomed on the horizon, I was born, followed two years later by my younger brother Bryan. The era of low farm gate prices and shortage of money to pay financial commitments, was followed by worry of a totally different nature in 1940, when it seemed almost certain that Britain would be invaded. My mother often remarked that there was a widespread feeling among farmers, that although the country required every ounce of food the farms could produce, some farmers questioned the wisdom of planting crops for Hitler. During all this time my mother was supporting the war effort to the hilt by baking cakes and selling jams and preserved fruits to raise funds for the Red Cross and other war time charities. In the meantime my father put in immensely long hours on the farm, as many farm men had been called up. His nights, once he had finished work on the farm, were spent patrolling the surrounding countryside as an air raid warden and special constable.

Both of my parents were stalwart supporters of St Leonard's church with my father serving 40 years as church warden from 1937, and my mother spending many years as treasurer, and then church warden after my father's death. She gave generously of her time filling stalls at money making events with produce that she had made. She crocheted linen for the alter frontals, arranged flowers in the east window and took part in the church cleaning rota well into her 90s.

My father was a highly respected cattle judge officiating at all shows where Lincoln Reds were exhibited, particularly enjoying showing cattle himself. He supported Lincolnshire agriculture in innumerable ways from Chief Steward at the Lincolnshire Show to being a long standing member of Louth NFU, having a particularly difficult job as branch chairman during the 1953 East coast floods, when he was responsible for coordinating flood relief and compensation.

CHAPTER 3
An American Connection

A sudden shaft of bright light draws my attention back to reality. I see our big Massey tractor with its attached 7 furrow reversible plough come to the end of its long run across the length of Pub field, then as the polished mirror like bodies rotate before heading back across the field they reflect the sun's rays in dazzling brilliance. Just beyond the tractor and plough lies The Orchards - my grandfather Henry Smith's retirement home until his death in 1955 at the age of 93. Henry Smith was one of 3 brothers and 3 sisters born in 1862 at Bunkers Hill Farm, Welton le Wold near Louth where his father John Smith was waggoner on the Welton estate. Young Henry left the village school at Welton le Wold aged 10 in 1872 and found work on the estate where his father and older brother John worked. A young boy's work at that time would have involved scaring crows from either newly sown grain or ripening corn, or droving cattle or sheep, followed at other times of the year by leading a horse and wagon in the hay or harvest field, in order that other farm workers could load the crop.

Henry was ambitious and certainly did not relish the prospect of being laid off work, thus facing the alternative of either the workhouse or being one of the almost 100,000 men who had left agriculture between 1871 and 1881, to find work in towns and cities. He abhorred the prospect of working in a factory, as he enjoyed country life, enjoying no finer recreation than to be armed with his shotgun, accompanied by his 2 dogs shooting rabbits, crows or pigeons.

It must have been with a sense of excitement born of frustration and hopelessness that at the age of 23 he joined hundreds of other agricultural workers at Louth's Candelmas annual, hiring fair in 1886, and enquired if anyone would accompany him to the United States of America to seek work on the new lands that were opening up westwards. He managed to recruit two young chaps by the name of Dave Marshall and another fellow by the name of Joe, who like him saw little prospect of a farming future in England at a time of ever lowering farm prices and wages. They bade farewell to family and friends in April 1886 and set off for Liverpool in the hope of securing a cheap passage to America.

Low priced transport supplied by the new railway systems, that were starting to straddle the North American continent, and the advent of cheaper more reliable steam driven ships that were replacing sail, coupled with the ability to utilise large machinery on the prairies, ensured that overseas grain could substantially undercut the price that British farmers could produce grain for.

From 1850 – 1870 wheat averaged 52 shillings a quarter which equates to £2.60 for 4.5 cwt or 225 kilograms. (£11.55) ton.

By 1878 the price had dropped, and by 1886 had reduced much further to £1.55 a quarter. (£6.88) ton.

Britain, then, as has also been the case in recent years, thought little about maintaining a viable agricultural sector to feed its growing population as it was the only major grain growing country to fully repeal external grain import tariffs.

Henry had managed to save only a few pounds from working so he could only afford the very cheapest accommodation in steerage class on a steam packet ship to America. He along with his two companions landed in New York at Ellis Island on 20th June 1886 when Henry immediately set about finding farm work. He heard that men were needed fruit picking on the shores of Lake Michigan, so he sought out transport and journeyed across to the great lakes were he found employment with a Mr Good picking apricots until 4th November 1886, earning the princely sum of $64. (about £16 @ 1880s exchange rate). Henry found work difficult to come by during his first bitterly cold northern U.S. winter, experiencing levels of cold of such intensity that he must have seriously questioned his wisdom in leaving England. It was with some relief that he managed to find employment with Mr Binly near South Haven on the shore of Lake Michigan earning a paltry $25 for four months work. Between the end of March 1887 and the end of November 1887 he earned a grand total of $ 144 working for Mr W Plummer who also had a fruit growing enterprise at South Haven.

Henry Smith with his Brouko horse in California 1896. Maybe the one that severely injured him. See letters in the appendix.

Henry Smith standing on the back of a combine harvester in California 1896. This early combine was pulled by no less than 24 mules.

Three letters written to two of his sisters coupled with a note book that he wrote recording his earnings survive Henry's time in The United Sates and give an insight to his fortitude and resilience. See Appendix at the rear of the book. He stuck to his task, when many lesser men would have given up and returned to their families and friends enjoying a much more predictable life back in England. Following severe winter weather of extraordinary coldness, certainly to him, during his 18 months in Michigan he decided that although homesick, prospects for work in England were no better and if anything worse than when he left, so he decided to travel over to California in the far west. On 26th November 1887 he started his journey west, getting to Davisville near Sacramento, and began work with Mc Kune and Garnet on 12th December 1887 earning $233 before leaving their employment on 1st August 1888. In the three years between September 1888 and October 1891 he earned the princely sum of $1202 working for 4 other employers. His letters written to his sisters, graphically illustrate what a difficult life he led, when earning money must have been incredibly difficult. From the 1st October 1891 until 31 December 1892 he records having earned another $525. Finally from 31st December 1892 until 1st May 1893 he earned another $140. On the 29th March 1893 Henry Smith appeared before W B Hamilton who was clerk to the State of California, County of Sacramento and "was duly sworn upon his oath that it is his intention to become a CITIZEN OF THE UNITED STATES OF AMERICA attested and officially sealed".

In April 1893 he received a letter from home stating that his mother was dangerously ill so after seven years in America, the last six of which were spent in California, he decided on 1st May 1893 to take the long journey back East, followed by steamer over the Atlantic to see his family and friends in England.

I suspect that he would have arrived back in England towards the end of June 1893.and would have quickly established that agriculture was in a more severe depression - if that were possible - than when he had left. There is no record of his 63 year old mother Eleanor's health, but he does refer to her again in a later letter to Eliza dated February 1896 when he does not want the results of his own accident reported to her, for fear of causing her distress. (See his letter in the appendix).

Deciding that prospects in England were bleak he bade farewell to everyone in mid August and returned to America arriving back in Davisville, California on 8th October 1893.

Henry continued to work in California until 1900 when increasing concerns about his mother's health and the desire to see his brothers and sisters precipitated his return back home to England,

Both Henry's father, also called Henry, and his mother Eleanor Hewson came from the Scambelsby area, west of Louth.

His eldest sister Eliza married John Ladley the Scambelsby blacksmith, who suffered fatal injuries at the young age of 37 whilst breaking in a horse in February 1891. They did not have any children and she never remarried.

Henry's eldest brother, called John but nicknamed Jack, was a shepherd who married three times. His first wife came from Muckton and they had a son called John, (also known as Jack) but she died as the result of an illness when little John was only three years of age, so his widowed sister Eliza raised young John as if he were her own child.

His second wife had several children, but regrettably she also died as the consequence of illness so perhaps wisely his third wife, knowing the fate of the first two wives didn't have any children.

Henry's younger brother Bob Hewson Smith who never married went on to join his widowed sister Eliza and take on the blacksmith shop becoming the village blacksmith, whilst his younger sister Fanny married Fred Dixon and went to live at Retford were they had one son called Frank who married Dorothy who in turn had one son called John.

Typifying the high esteem that he held for his sisters on his return from America Henry lent Fanny £100 so that she and her husband Frank could purchase a house in Retford.

(In 2005 My wife and I called to see their only daughter Dorothy, who was still living in the same terraced house despite being well advanced in her 90s.)

When Henry finally returned to England in 1900 aged 38 he went to live with his second oldest sister Dinah and her husband Abraham Broddle who rented Glebe Farm, at Asterby. However within a couple of years the Broddles gave up the tenancy when they purchased a small farm at Fen Houses in South Somercotes. Henry decided to take on the farm tenancy following the Broddles departure and was lucky enough to find a young widow called Annie Wright who would keep house for him.

Annie was a sensible hard working woman with whom, in her adversity of losing her husband, Henry could empathise as he knew only too well how hard life could be. It was therefore unsurprising that he should think that she would be an ideal person to keep house for him. She obviously suited Henry because before long he asked her to marry him resulting in their marriage in 1906 and the birth of my mother Ellen in June 1908, followed by a son named Harry in November 1909.

Henry had kept the tenancy of Glebe Farm until 1916, when Colonel Fenwick who owned the Stenigot Estate offered him the tenancy of the 350 acre Wellsdale Farm which lay in a sheltered position in a deep wolds valley between the Bluestone Heath road and Donnington on Bain. The farm had a substantially built farmhouse and two recently constructed cottages, with excellent stabling for 8 heavy horses, but poor quality cattle yards that offered little cover.

Harry, Henry's only son joined his father on the farm in 1921 when it's quite possible that there was friction with his step brother Robert who was 10 years his senior. For whatever reason they didn't get on and Robert decided to join the armed services. Harry took over the farm in 1938 when he married Mary Freeborough, the Donington on Bain station masters daughter, and went to live in the farm house. My Grandfather then aged 76 along with my 66 year old grandmother thought that this was an appropriate time for them to retire and take life easier for their remaining years. They found the ideal property called The Orchards situated on Louth Road, North Cockerington that was within a mile of where his daughter, my mother, lived. It proved to be the ideal location as it had a good house and outbuildings along with a large orchard and a 12 acre grass field. He grazed the grass with his own stock for the first few years and then when it became too much for him, rented it out to Mr Charles Kent who had a small dairy farm a little further down the road.

Bearing in mind that Wellsdale was an isolated farm situated in the midst of thousands of acres of open countryside it must count as one of the most unlucky casualties of the Second World War. A stray German bomber was returning back to Germany after a night's bombing raid in the midlands and decided to jettison its remaining bombs before crossing the North Sea. Unluckily the bombs scored a direct hit on the farm completely destroying the pair of cottages and blowing the roof off the farmhouse just across the road. Harry and Mary and their small daughter Ann were evacuated to Mary's grandmother's house in Donington on Bain. In due course the estate repaired the house but they never returned to live there and Harry soon relinquished the tenancy. Harry was then able to secure the tenancy of the Glebe Farm at Yarburgh but found the heavy marshland soils a completely different proposition to the easy working wold land at Donington on Bain. I remember in the late 40s accompanying my parents to Sunday tea after which Harry would take my father and I for a ride around the farm. Even at my then tender age, I had an overriding impression of wet fields and rather poor looking crops. Perhaps if the land had benefitted by the widespread under draining schemes that were so prevalent a little more than a decade later and Harry had had the horsepower that was available in the future he may well have made a success of the farm. However the accumulated difficulties of heavy land, poor machinery and general lack of expertise led him to give up the farm in 1952 at the age of 43 and retreat to the 40 acres of land at Red Hill Asterby that my Grandfather had purchased with his savings on his return from America.

Harry then rented the 100 acre Glebe Farm across the road that his father had farmed 40 years earlier. In due course Harry gave up the Glebe Farm tenancy and erected a house on his Red Hill land, supplementing his income by helping auctioneers pen sheep at local livestock markets, before retiring to Welton near Lincoln and living close to his daughter Ann.

CHAPTER 4
EARLY MEMORIES

Suddenly my reverie of thoughts are rudely interrupted by the ear splitting sound of two RAF Euro Fighters streaking in an elaborate curve over the marsh as they head towards the Wolds and RAF Coningsby beyond.

As the rapidly disappearing aircraft leave a trail of black smoke across the sky my memory turns to aircraft of quite a different type during the last war, when on such an evening as this, I recall seeing formations of Lancaster Bombers stretching from horizon to horizon, as they congregated in the sky above this part of east England to prepare for their nightly bombing missions into Germany. The reverberating sound of hundreds of throbbing aircraft engines from scores of bomber bases in the East Midlands, made an indelible impression on my young mind. Lincolnshire had the highest concentration of bomber bases anywhere in the Country so it was probably unsurprising that much later in the night I would again hear the sound of aircraft as they passed overhead on their return to local bases such as Ludford Magna, Binbrook, Kelstern, Hemswell etc. Regrettably many did not return and others that had been damaged came limping back to their bases, with some making emergency landings at airfields such as Manby, whose hangers I can see only a couple of miles away.

I clearly remember walking home with my parents from the six o clock evensong church service, on a beautiful Sunday evening in September 1944, when to our complete astonishment discovered that during the duration of the service every grass field in the village had become saturated with hundreds of army transport vehicles, and thousands of army personal dressed in full combat dress.

Next morning when I got up, I discovered they had all disappeared. Had I imagined it, or was it part of a dream? Of course it wasn't a dream because the night before my mother had supplied them with all the eggs she had in the house, so the only reminder of our visitors were a few piles of eggshells and tyre marks in the gateways. I believe, looking back now, that these brave men were part of the air born paratroops force who attempted to capture the bridge over the Rhine at Arnhem. As I gaze around me I can see the spot where a German aircraft was shot down near Marsh Lane and remember the fierce fire that engulfed the barley stacks, with a total loss of all the unthreshed grain.

Another aircraft crashed just beyond the Park Field and to this day small bits of aluminium and Perspex can still be picked up whenever the field is cultivated. Bombs were dropped throughout the area, those that exploded left deep craters particularly one in the corner of 40 acre field where a mound of greyish brown earth had been thrown up. Venturing up to the crater side, not knowing quite what I might see it was with a feeling of anticlimax to observe a pond of turgid brown water.

I was born in 1937, so consequently my earliest recollections as a child relate to war time food rationing, clothing coupons and all the restrictions that were imposed by a country fighting for its very survival. I remember so clearly asking my mother what the papers would find to write about now that the war had ended in April 1945. As school children it was constantly instilled in us not to pick up or touch anything that we might find, regardless of how intriguing it might look.

The Rev James Smart who was vicar of North and South Cockerington with Alvingham, lived in the high roofed gothic style rectory next door to North Cockerington C of E School and frequently came into the classroom to take religious lessons, but occasionally he would be accompanied by an army officer who would talk to us about bombs that we might discover. Following a talk, illustrated with pictures that were deliberately intended to shock us by showing children who had sustained horrific injuries caused by exploding ordnance, we were instructed to follow them into the extensive grounds of the vicar's, next door, rectory garden. Arranged around the perimeter of one of the vicarages largest lawns lay scores of grey sinister looking projectiles, many with pointed tips, bulbous middles and finned tails. After the military man had carefully explained the significance of all this German weaponry to us and what might happen when it exploded, the Rev Smart went on to reinforce the points that the officer had made.

"You must never touch anything that you may find as you walk home or when you are playing", he would insist. "Even the most innocent looking object might be a bomb that will kill or injure you if you touch it".

I remember that the small 'butterfly bombs' with their delicate wing like structure looked to be incapable of doing any harm to us or indeed anything else, so it was very difficult for us to comprehend that these innocuous looking objects were a threat, rather they represented something we might actually search for because as a consequence of war time shortages we didn't have interesting toys to play with. In spite of the succession of implored warnings we never the less scoured the grass fields searching for strips of silver foil called chaff ? that German bombers dropped in an effort to confuse our Radar. Although this rural area was never intended as a target a great many bombs were dumped here by returning German bombers who had not successfully completed their missions over midland cities.

Rationing, particularly of sweets, meant that anything edible with a sweet nature would be particularly appealing. It was little wonder that we searched in the cattle cake for sweet locust (Carob) bean pods, included in the concentrate rations for our sheep and cattle to supplement their diet. Liquorice root became surrogate sweets to us as it could be purchased from the village shop, without sweet coupons when the sweet juice could be sucked from the stringy fibres. However it incurred mother's displeasure as it left fingers, mouth and lips heavily stained with a brown, indelible dye.

Growing up in the 1940's my younger brother Bryan and I would frequently go for long walks across the grass Park Field, that had originally provided a tree lined drive to South Cockerington Hall, and entered what we always thought of as the mysterious and exciting bottom plantations. These woods, bordering the Greyfleet beck, were largely comprised of elm saplings that had re-grown from mature elm trees which had been felled during the First World War to provide planks for First World War trenches and tunnels in Northern France. Elm proved to be the perfect timber for retaining earth because its complex grain structure made it difficult to split, and it also had the additional benefit of being able to withstand wet conditions without rotting.

The trees formed a dense wood perhaps fifty feet in height and consequently proved an exciting and irresistible place for us to play. Sadly all of the elm trees in the woods by the beck side succumbed to Dutch elm disease in the nineteen sixties and seventies completely killing them all. Over the succeeding years we cleared the dead trees away for firewood, then in 1992 we replanted all of this old woodland along with a considerable area of adjoining land with a mixed variety of broad leaved trees to create a lasting legacy for the benefit of generations to come.

The water flowing in the beck is generally crystal clear and tranquil so that it's quite easy to see shoals of shining stickle backs either darting for cover in the deeper pools, or skimming over translucent pebbles that glint in the sunlight percolating the canopy of overhanging branches. However in times of heavy rain the beck swells to a raging torrent as it carries enormous volumes of angry brown storm water from the eastern escarpment of the wolds, south of Louth, to the sea.

I have fond memories of following the course of the beck on a bright spring day and emerging on the western side of the wood in the direction of Stewton. The beck which forms the boundary between South Cockerington and Grimoldby led to our Forty acre field. A particular highlight of this spring time trek was to continue the walk via Hoyes farmyard across to Monks Dyke where it bordered Conscience Hill looking for the scattered clumps of early primroses that grew on the dyke side hoping to gather a bunch of flowers to take home for Mother.

At this time Conscience Hill was divided into three fields with the eastern, largely flat, twenty six acres under grass, and judging by a depression that looked rather like a dry ditch bed running through the centre of the field indicated that in earlier times it too had been divided. Beyond the grass field was a line of moderate sized trees that many years ago had been a hawthorn hedge but because it hadn't been trimmed for perhaps the last fifty years had become completely outgrown, offering little protection as a fence against livestock. However the boundary had been re-enforced with rusty sea defence scaffold piping to form a stock proof fence.

A dilapidated wooden shed with an orange pan-tiled roof stood in the centre of the boundary, adjacent to a gate which led into the central fifteen acres of Conscience Hill.

During the early months of the second world war when there was a very real danger of imminent invasion, scaffolding pipes were erected on the flat open beaches from Cleethorpes to Theddlethorpe, in an elaborate matrix of steel that resembled a gigantic grandstand looking out to sea. It was felt that this wide beach would make an ideal beachhead for the enemy to bring in landing craft containing tanks and their support vehicles to supply the invasion.

After the war the beaches were cleared of mines, and local farmers were encouraged to collect this iron piping for free. In most cases it was re-erected into three and four barred fences around grass fields.

Our farm in common with many Marsh farms collected enormous quantities of this iron piping and accompanying fastening clips, which by this stage were heavily pitted with rust. The piping was stored on the ground in horizontal heaps which due to the salt water and the consequential ingression of salt sand down the pipes rapidly hastened the rusting process. The iron piping was used extensively all over the farm for a wide variety of uses, including of course, many miles of fencing, which although rusty did an admirable job until the effects of the salt eventually rusted through the iron rendering it useless.

Sea defence piping erected as fencing around livestock fields. This photograph which was taken in the late 1960s following particularly heavy rain, shows how the piping was already starting to rust away.

The middle 15 acre field that contained the highest point of Conscience Hill, was bordered on its western boundary by another overgrown hawthorn hedge that divided it from the 15 acre field known as Far Platt, which along with '40 acre' shares the distinction of being the most westerly fields on the farm. As an eight year old I was fascinated to know what a magpie's egg looked like and wanted to add one to my egg collection, a very popular hobby with country boys at that time. Seeing one of their domed nests in the densest part of one of the large hawthorn bushes, I clambered up the trunk and squeezed my way among the branches doing my upmost to avoid being pricked with the spiny thorns that sprang from every twig and branch of the bush, then rather precariously stretched an arm through the woven twig entrance of the nest. To my astonishment I soon discovered that the nest had been colonised by a pair of kestrel when one of the furious birds emerged from within the twigs and set about attacking me, I quickly retreated down the branches of the thorny bush. After that I was much more careful where I placed my hand.

In those seemingly far off days harvesting was still quite an involved process that comprised cutting the grain with a binder, followed by placing the sheaves in tent like formations all over the field in order that the corn could dry, after which, the sheaves were taken to the farmyard for stacking prior to threshing during the winter months. I along with other farm children looked forward to threshing days, especially when the stack of sheaves was reduced to head height. As sheaves were removed from the stack it exposed dazed looking mice unsure for a second or two which direction to run. In their moments of confusion it enabled us to wack them with a stick before they managed to dart away. If a stack was not threshed until March or April, numbers of Rats and Mice multiplied to very high levels due to the unlimited amount of food available for them to eat over the winter period. I have good reason to recall one such occasion as I waited in keen anticipation to wack my next mouse with a poised stick. The man on the corn stack lifted the next sheaf of corn, but rather than see the expected mouse an enormous rat jumped out and dived headlong into the front of my unbuttoned open shirt. I am not sure who was the more terrified, me or the rat, as the frantic animal raced around my body rather like a motor cyclist on a wall of death using my body as a circular race track. In the process it left me with painful scratch marks around my middle before it finally made its escape by means of the way that it got in. After that I always ensured that my shirt was tightly fastened to the neck, though my short trousers with their wide leg openings did rather worry me.

Looking across to the north, and coming to within a few feet of the junction where the road continues on to Yarburgh, Covenham and Fulstow I can easily see the distinctive white walls of White Barn which are sharply illuminated by the evening sun. The farm buildings are a very well know local landmark standing on a slightly elevated position a field away from the river Lud and Louth canal to the south. As I shift my sight a little further to the right I can identify the twin stone towers of the two churches of Alvingham and North Cockerington. Every Ascension day, from the time I started school at the age of four I clearly remember walking with the rest of the North Cockerington C of E School pupils over the footbridges that spanned both the Louth canal and River Lud, to attend the service held there. The school, with its high arched ceiling, enormous gothic north facing window, and coke burning pot-bellied stove, comprised a large room for the older children and a smaller one for the infants. I now look back on my early school days with a great deal of affection, in stark contrast to the austere regime that I experienced as a boarder at De Aston Grammar School where I went just two weeks beyond my eleventh birthday in September 1948.

Harry Brooks was the genial, inspirational headmaster at North Cockerington C of E, who proved to be a good friend whilst at the same time being an excellent teacher who provided encouragement as he instilled a great work ethic coupled with a set of sound moral values. For many years during his long period as headmaster he played a leading role in Cockerington village life and local affairs, using the schoolroom as a platform to induce community spirit within the area at a time when travelling was severely limited because of wartime fuel rationing. On a make-shift, trestle table stage, erected at one end of the large school room, he produced and performed in a wide variety of plays and other entertainments for the villagers, in addition to using the room for a whole raft of other social events throughout the winter months. Whist drives that raised money for The Lindsey Blind Society were one of his great passions; they were not only hugely enjoyable social events but helped a very worthy local charity. Quite regularly during the summer months he would continue our education within his one acre garden at the other end of the village, where he kept numerous hives of bees that was yet another of his very keen interests. His cheerful enthusiasm combined with practical instruction on growing plants gave us a wonderful insight into elementary biology and science of the soil that was made all the more interesting when he allowed us to take some of the garden produce home.

Suddenly my eyes are alerted to a flash to the east of me, as the sun strikes a car windscreen rounding Pub corner. I am reminded of Jack and Mrs Patrick who used to live there at the Post Office. I never knew

Mrs Patrick's first name as I can never recall anyone addressing her in terms other than Mrs Patrick. I do remember though that she was a very substantially built lady with a round jovial face and a happy smiling disposition, and although her silver hair was always tied into a bun, it rather resembled an untidy bird's nest with unruly hair poking out in all directions. She was a motherly figure with voluptuous breasts preserved under a green herring bone patterned coat that she constantly wore even during the warmest days of summer.

In those far off days few people owned a car as almost everyone travelled by bus. Consequently little traffic passed her house at the crossroads, yet she was almost obsessive in reminding us of the perils that might befall us if we weren't careful crossing the road, and to be especially wary of vehicles on the rest of our daily mile walk to school at North Cockerington. Generally the only thing that we met was a drove of cattle that were been driven along the road. In addition to running the sub post office from her kitchen, she stocked Bellamys "pop", which was an irresistible drink for children rationed to 2 ounces of sweets per week. After all these years I can still recollect the keen anticipation of drinking a bottle of pop. The hissing sound of escaping gas as I carefully unscrewed the black stopper from the top of the bottle, allowed my nose to pick up the smell of ice cream soda or dandelion and burdock carried on minute airborne droplets, so that when I took the first sip it seemed to taste like nectar. The "pop" cost 6d, (2. 1/2p) and was sold in large glass bottles fastened by a black hard rubber screw stopper with an orange rubber washer that kept it air tight. The bottles had a return value of 1d, so it encouraged us to find bottles that people had discarded in order that we were able to finance even more full bottles at no extra cost to ourselves. Mrs Patrick's sub Post Office was quite a low tech affair as she dispensed stamps and postal orders from a well thumbed folder kept on the table immediately behind the door leading into her tiny living room.

In a central position on the back wall beyond the table was a small, black, fireside cooking range with two well worn chairs placed on either side of the chimney breast. Beside the wall immediately opposite the back door stood a brown leather chaise longue that fitted snugly between one of the fire side chairs and another door that led into the 'best' room into which the external post-box protruded. I don't ever recall Mr and Mrs Patrick ever going away for a holiday as the post box was fitted into the front wall of the house and was generally cleared from inside. Mrs Patrick usually delivered mail by cycle around the village. I remember how she used to wheeze and gasp at our back door as she delved into a bag slung across her portly frame and extracted our mail, then she would have a chat as she regained her breath before continuing with her deliveries. Her smiling countenance was always a tonic as she would laughingly relay the latest morsel of village gossip, such as,

"Did yer knaw thet Mrs Jackson wus taken bad lest neet,
ay, they ed ter fitch docter te er."

Then passing a postcard to mother she was just as likely to pass an observation.

"I'm pleased Gladys iz aving a gud time",

or on handing over a letter might remark,

"Yu've got a litter frum andover sem es mister Humerstun".

Mrs Patrick was a true friend to everyone in the village and sadly the community was the poorer when both she and husband Jack left, and the sub post office closed.

Sixty years ago the responsibility for routine highway maintenance tasks such as digging out roadside, drainage gully's and scything vegetation that might obscure the vision of people travelling on the road, was undertaken by local county council highways employees called lengths men. Jack Patrick was such a man and he was responsible for the care of the roadsides in our immediate district. Jack was a tall craggy man, with a heavily lined rather gaunt looking features whose flat cap struggled to retain a mop of unruly silver hair. During the summer months he wore an unbuttoned, dark coloured waistcoat that originally might have been a constituent of a previous Sunday best three piece suit. This item of clothing was now giving Jack serviceable duty as a useful part of his everyday work attire, partially covering a collarless striped shirt with the long sleeves loosely rolled up to his elbows. Jacks trousers were suspended by a set of wide braces that terminated in three pairs of leather thongs that fastened over buttons sewn to the outside of his trousers. A little lower down lengths of loosely tied binder twine were tied around each leg at calf height, finally on his feet irrespective of summer or winter he always wore a pair of heavy hob nailed boots. The old adage of belt and braces might well have been coined for Jack because in addition to his braces he wore a three inch wide heavy duty leather belt that encircled his lean frame, so there was never the slightest fear of him losing his trousers. All the tools he required for his work were carried on his bicycle, brush and shovel securely fastened with leather straps under the crossbar, and a coat carefully tied onto the carrier behind his seat. Jack would chat with anyone who would stop as they passed by. He loved to recount his experiences during the 1st World War, and describe more recent anecdotes from his home guard days in the 2nd World War.

On the occasions he saw me, coming home from school, he would always stop, then with the aid of his shovel prop his bike in an upright position by the roadside verge. Gripping his brush shaft with both hands he would lean in a comfortable position to have a word, usually prefacing his first remark by saying,

"Whets thu sckooal mester taut yah todaya?"

I would describe some of the things that I had done that day, when almost as though he hadn't been listening to what I had been saying, he would carry on in an almost dream like nostalgic manner with an observation made scores of times before to me. I was reminded of it years later, when Trig, a character with the part of a council road sweeper in the comedy series Fools and Horses made a similar observation.

"Thay giv me this ere brush whin I started we um an ive hed it awl thu time". When I said *"it's lasted well"*, he replied

"It's ad a few new edds an three or fower new shefts."

On the arrival of drier days in summer Jacks brush would be fully employed sweeping loose stones and grit from the road side in preparation for tarring. This operation was always a great source of excitement for us, as early in the morning plumes of dense, black smoke heralded the arrival of the heavy, steam roller with its tall, black chimney and its open curved roof cab. It made its ponderous clanking way from Louth towing an iron wheeled water tanker, which in turn pulled a faded green painted cabin. In reality the cabin was little more than a hut mounted on iron wheels with a metal chimney protruding through its dome shaped roof. It carried coal to fuel not only the fire grate inside, but also the steam roller itself, whilst also acting as a rest room. It also provided the engine drivers living accommodation as he was obliged to stay with the steam roller overnight in order to have it fired up with steam for the next day's work. I remember the engine driver as being a short, stocky man with bright, red cheeks, wearing a tight fitting jacket which strained to meet around his substantial midriff. On his head he wore a black, railway driver's, peaked cap, which along with the rest of his clothes was heavily engrained with a combination of soot and grease. Great care was always taken in selecting a suitable, well drained position on a wide, roadside verge to unhitch the train of vehicles because of their great weight. Very soon the tar lorry appeared and deposited a steaming layer of pungent smelling black tar over the road surface, then Jack along with the other highways lengths men, who now made up the tarring gang shovelled stone chippings on to the wet tar from either a reversing partly tipped lorry, or wheeled them in a wheelbarrow from heaps of chippings staged along the roadside. Finally the driver of the heavy, steam roller leaning out of his cab, and with the rollers tall chimney belching clouds of black smoke, spun a small silver steering wheel as he eased the machine from the road side on to the freshly laid chippings. With a great deal of clanking and escaping steam the massive iron wheels of the roller obliterated the grey slag chippings into a table top flat surface. The driver manoeuvred the formidable machine with the greatest dexterity, completely confident in his own ability, no doubt as a result of many years spent in intimate contact with it.

My father with a couple of foxes that would annihilate a henhouse of chickens if woe be told the slide wasn't secured at nightfall. 1956.

From a very early age I was given a regular routine of tasks to undertake after I returned home from school, commencing with going round three or four chicken huts situated in nearby fields to collect the hen's eggs. I remember that I was always apprehensive about removing broody hens from the eggs as they had a nasty habit of pecking as I prised the eggs from beneath them. From time to time, particularly if I was in a rush to get back home, I would cycle round the fields to save time by hanging the handle of the metal bucket, containing the eggs, over one side of the handle-bars. It unfortunately tended to unbalance the bike making it difficult to steer, with the result that occasionally I fell off. Broken eggs are hard to repair and Mother didn't appreciate scrambled eggs mixed with shells.

My next job prior to getting mains water was to pump water from the well situated by the house back door, up to the large water tank within the house that provided all of our domestic water. I had to pump until such time as the water came out of the overflow pipe when I would know that the tank was full to capacity.

Finally as darkness fell I had to close the chicken hut slides to prevent foxes gaining entry and slaughtering the hens during the night. I remember that I used to run as fast as my legs could carry me as I went from hut to hut in the various fields. Some of the farm men had told me frightening tales of rats emerging from under the huts at night time and giving chase. Then I was always fearful that something or somebody might be lurking in the deepening shadows because there were also wildly, fearful stories circulating amongst us children of the dreaded "Hun", and what might befall us if we were caught.

Inevitably my childhood memories are associated either with the war or the deprivations and shortages associated with rationing. Shortly before Christmas a man from Nottingham would come to the house, to collect all Mother's dressed poultry comprising chickens, ducks and geese, that she had spent the greater part of the year rearing. On one occasion such was the dire need for meat during those war years that the man, on seeing a pile of rats that had been caught following a day's threshing, asked my father what would be happening to the carcases. My father told him that they would be buried, whereupon he said, could he take them. I strongly suspect that they would have formed the meat content of some exotically named dish in a midlands restaurant.

During those years country children had to make their own entertainment but my brother and I were quite fortunate as, prior to getting mains electricity, my parents were privileged to have a wireless. However this could only be operated by a lead acid accumulator that had to be charged weekly in Tom Topliss's shop situated in the Cornmarket in Louth. Those early wirelesses as they were known required a great deal of power to operate the valves which rapidly drained the accumulator, consequently listening time was strictly rationed to comedy programmes such as ITMA and the Saturday night radio play, interspersed with the news and Churchill's uplifting speeches as an antidote to Lord Haw Haws, "Germany calling", with its moral sapping propaganda. From October 1946 as the last bars of "The Devils Gallop" faded into the ether, we would group around the radio to hear the latest nightly episode of the serial 'Dick Barton special agent'. The adventures of Dick and his two sidekicks were enormously addictive, recording more than 15 million listeners at the peak.

Our paraffin filled Aladdin Lamp with its incandescent mantle glowing white hot gave a much better illumination than an ordinary oil lamp, with the result that it gave a decent light for reading so that I was able to entertain myself with a book leading to me having a lifelong interest in literature.

Soon after mains water was connected to the village in 1946 my parents carried out some major improvements to the house that involved moving the bathroom to another upstairs room resulting in the old bathroom becoming my bedroom.

The following spring I was regularly woken soon after dawn, by a rustling and scraping sound under the floor boards. I discovered that a starling, noticing a gap in the outside brickwork where a waste pipe had been removed, decided that this was a prime location to establish a nest. One day when my parents were out, I was determined to do something about the situation, so armed with a sturdy screwdriver I levered up the short length of floor board in the bedroom immediately above the hole in the wall and removed the birds nest. I figured that if I was going to make a permanent job, then I needed to block up the hole from the outside and stop the bird getting in again. So I went down to the farmyard and found a ladder and half a brick. Unfortunately as the hole was directly under the window and as it was a long ladder it meant that when the top of the ladder was placed on the window sill the foot of the ladder extended a long way back.

Undeterred carrying my brick I scaled the ladder, and then just when I was about to place the brick in the hole, with my arm almost fully extended, the foot of the wooden ladder lost what little grip it had on the smooth tiled floor of the causeway resulted in it sliding backwards. I crashed down, with my face and particularly my nose, taking the full impact as it connected with an outside tap that as a part of the alterations had recently been fixed to that part of the exterior wall. When my parents returned home, it must have been with mounting alarm that they followed a trail of blood leading inside the house. They were naturally horrified to see me with blood still pouring down my face as it dripped in scarlet streams onto my white school shirt leaving sticky red pools across the tiled kitchen floor. I was rushed off to see Dr Morton, a surgeon friend of my father at Louth Hospital, who confirmed that I would live, but had suffered multiple fractures to my nose. However, he thought that due to my extensive facial swelling it would have to heal in its present state. In about 8 months time I would have to return to the hospital when he would break the nasal bones once again so that he could make a better job of straightening it.

After 4 months I found it impossible to breathe through my nose, as tissue had completely closed each nostril so my operation was brought forward. Needless to say, my weeks stay in hospital was a painful experience as I had to endure lengths of rope like material inserted up each nostril.

At a later date with the aid of a shorter ladder and Walter Evison the garthman standing on its foot, I successfully cemented half a brick into the drain hole and finally put paid to birds nesting under the floorboards of my bedroom.

Following the removal of sheaves when a corn stack was threshed the steadle of dry straw that originally had been laid over the ground in order to keep the bottom sheaves dry was now composed of partially rotted straw. As a child, and I must say it seems pretty sad when I reflect on it now, I could amuse myself for hours building rows of small stacks of this now partially rotted material with an old muck fork whose tines had worn down rendering it of little use for normal farm work.

Aerial view of Hill House farm in 1952. Note the open crew yards and the stacks to the rear of the farmyard. The building on the extreme left housed the threshing machine. The "glasshouse" is the building now reroofed immediately to the left of the new Dutch barn. The range of buildings that lie across the top of the picture were built as horse stables. It was inside the second building on the right that both Alistair and I were badly mauled by a cow one New Years eve. The square fenced off in the field to the right of the row of stables was constructed of the sea defence piping and was used as a calf creep. See also the two chicken houses and the cattle stable in the top right of the photograph that produced some of the finest Cockerington champion cattle.

The farm buildings at Hill House Farm have changed beyond recognition over the years, and now bear little relationship to the layout of 60 years ago when many of the buildings were constructed with wooden boarded walls and clay pan tile roofs.

One of the buildings at the extreme north west of the farmyard was called the glasshouse crew, because part of the roof was glazed, although from my earliest recollection I never knew it to be used for growing plants, as the roof was in pretty poor condition with missing panes of glass and broken glazing bars. The building had been subdivided inside to form an L shaped crew yard, with a wooden sided stable about 12 feet square in one corner that was large enough to accommodate a cow and calf. I remember, when I was probably no more than 8 years old, accompanying Walter Evison, who was the garthman responsible for feeding the cattle during the winter at that yard, as he carried a forkful of hay into the stable to feed to a newly calved Lincoln Red cow. The cow evidently thought I represented some sort of threat to her calf as she immediately charged me, pinning me tight against the wooden boarded wall with her two forward facing horns straddling my chest, when they became embedded into the wooden planking. I wonder what must have been passing through Walters head when the realisation hit him on what might have happened.

In spite of all the wartime restrictions and the unavailability of so many things we take for granted today I had a happy childhood with caring parents who only wanted the best for their two sons.

During the Second World War and for several years following its conclusion petrol was still rationed, and as no new cars were being manufactured it was almost impossible to purchase a car of any sort with the result that almost everyone travelled to Louth by bus. My father shared a 1937 Austin 10 car with his brother Jack that was garaged in a curved roofed Nissen type building across a couple of paddocks at South View Farm. As there was little spare fuel I don't think that I ever travelled much further than a few miles from home before I was 8 years old in August 1945. Mother though would regularly take my brother and I by bus on the 4 miles to Louth, when she shopped for clothes or took us for a haircut at Remingtons in Aswell Street. We used to join the bus at the point where Pedlar Lane joined the main road, when such was the demand to travel by bus particularly on market days or Saturday afternoons that the bus companies ran several relief coaches, with the driver passing a thumb over his left shoulder to indicate that he was full but there were other buses following behind him.

At around 5pm in the 1940 and 50s the Market Place and Mercer Row areas in Louth buzzed with activity as people thronged onto a multitude of buses that were lined up in ranks, with buses departing for destinations throughout the surrounding district. They were drawn up in such numbers with duplicate buses adding to the principle ones, it was very easy to catch the wrong bus.

In 1946 my father bought a pre-war Austin 12 which despite the stringent petrol rationing still in place gave him more independence that allowed him to give us special treats with a tour around the countryside on fine summer evenings.

In early February 1947 my parents went away for a few days holiday in London, which was their first holiday together since they were married in 1932. They travelled by train from Louth station to London leaving my six year old brother and I with my 85 year old grandfather Smith and his housekeeper Mrs Kemp at his home, The Orchards in North Cockerington. Unfortunately their holiday coincided with one of the coldest winters for over 100 years that created widespread disruption of both road and rail traffic. To make matters worse the country was still in the grip of war time rationing with not only shortages of food but heat and light as well. I remember that my brother and I had been invited to A birthday party in the village whilst they were away, but as the main road was continually filling with snow drifts, Grandfather sent me down to the village in the morning to say that we would be unable to come that afternoon because of the snow. Very few folk owned telephones at that time, and my grandfather never owned one and probably never used one in his life.

Life in the village during that long severe winter reverted back to conditions that would have been familiar to anyone living more than100 years previous because for weeks on end the main road to Louth was blocked with snow despite being dug out by hand on many occasions. The railway line from Grimsby to London was kept open by a combination of snow ploughs mounted on the front of trains and even hand digging in places where the drifted snow was too deep for the snow ploughs. Bread and other vital provisions were carried over the fields from Louth by hand drawn sledge as the local delivery vans were unable to travel.

CHAPTER 5
How things were

Village communities such as those in South Cockerington were served by a great variety of tradesmen who came into the village on a weekly basis, with some, such as the baker's delivery rounds men from Teasdale and Willerton and Slater Eyre in Louth visiting customers twice a week. A short thick set man wearing a fawn raincoat topped by a dashing broad brimmed grey trilby hat was Slater Eyres regular bread rounds man who delivered bread to our house. I remember how he used to negotiate the slippery blue bricks that led to the back door, (which were the cause of my downfall with the ladder), clutching an enormous woven wicker basket packed tight with both steam and crusty loaves, in addition to cakes and currant buns. It always seemed to me to be such a waste of effort as mother only ever purchased one crusty loaf. However on very special occasions she might purchase four current buns that were made of slightly sweetened bread, and because of wartime rationing just the odd currant. Mother used to constantly remark about how grey the bread looked, but that could have been a combination of incorporating softer wheat in the flour due to wartime difficulties in importing Canadian hard wheat, coupled with the lack of a whitening agent.

Mrs Marshalls tiny 10 x8 feet shop in Chapel lane was remarkable for the amazing number of different lines that she carried in an incredibly small area, with many village people purchasing most of what they needed from her shop. Alternative supplies were delivered by grocery vans such as Traffords from Alvingham , Sowbys from Grainthorpe and Larders of Louth, who visited a great many rural households every week on their respective rounds. These vans were a mobile extension of village and town shops, stocking all regular necessities for people with little or no transport. It was a godsend to have goods delivered direct to the door.

Although milk was delivered around the village every day, our milk came from a house cow on the farm that the herdsman hand milked twice daily. The smaller quantity of afternoons milking came to our house whilst the much greater quantity from the mornings milking was divided between my uncle Jacks House and the herdsman's household. As soon as the herdsman delivered the milk to the door Mother would immediately pour the milk through a fine meshed, muslin strainer. It removed the odd cobweb that may have dropped into the bucket from the cow stable roof, or more usually bits of straw that the cow might have flicked into the bucket with her tail to say nothing of the odd bit of dry cow muck that dropped from the cows teats. She poured the milk into a series of wide topped 6 inch deep enamelled bowls that gave the milk the maximum amount of surface area for the cream to rise, from the cooling milk. After a couple of days the cream was skimmed off the milk and added to the previous skimming's until there was a sufficient quantity to make it worthwhile spending half an hour turning the handle of the butterchurn Prior to getting mains electricity in 1947, when the cream could be stored in a fridge, butter was usually churned every 4 to 5 days during the warmer summer months, and perhaps twice as long during the winter months. Although salt was added to assist the butters keeping quality it never the less soon acquired a slightly rancid taste, especially during the summer.

From my position up here I would have been able to observe a steady stream of other deliveries bringing goods into the village, in addition to the bread, grocery and milk tradesmen.

On a still day I might just have heard the rhythmical sound made by the hooves of George Graves, the Grimoldby coalman's horse's, and the ringing tones of his metal wheeled dray. Sitting with his legs dangling from the front corner of the four wheeled wagon, whilst propping his back against the open bags of coal, he delivered around the village on a weekly basis. The majority of his customers might only purchase a couple of bags or so at a time, which would be sufficient to last them the week. I remember that in addition to collecting coal from the goods sidings at the adjacent Grimoldby station, he had a small paddock immediately to the north of Grimoldby church where he kept his wagon and grazed his horse.

Almost everyone kept a few chickens at the bottom of the garden to lay eggs whilst the cockerels were fattened for eating.

Unlike today when chicken is mass produced under factory farming conditions with consequently very low prices, a roast chicken was then regarded as something of a luxury only to be eaten on special occasions as it was much more expensive than beef.

A train entering Grimoldby station from Mablethorpe. The line closed 3rd December 1960. Almost a mile of the old track runs through the centre of our Eastfield Farm which we still use as a farm road.

Many country folk also kept a pig or two in a pig sty at the bottom of the garden, feeding them on household scraps supplemented with BOCM meal delivered by one of George Merrikin's mustard coloured lorries. Mr Garlant was the local Levers representative for animal foodstuffs with a depot in a nissen hut situated in Grimoldby Station goods yard.

It's not widely appreciated that whilst food and clothing were rationed similar restrictions were imposed on animal foodstuffs, they could only be obtained by strictly regulated coupons. (During the winter months mobile slaughtermen such as Arthur Benton or Henry Parker would kill the pigs and cut up the carcases for preserving with salt when the pig would provide meat for most of the year.) The daily retinue of household services was completed with Mr Enderby cycling around the village delivering daily newspapers and Mrs Patrick's postal deliveries.

The majority of goods and services were then delivered direct to households, in contrast to the position today were people have to travel to collect their requirements, though in some ways things are now coming full circle with home deliveries from internet shopping. Many people therefore had little need to travel with many not even travelling the 4 miles to Louth for months on end. George Hoyes, when over 60, assured us on many occasions that he had never travelled further than Lincoln, that being on the occasion of the Royal Shows visit to the city just after

The mud and stud cottage opposite Hill House farm yard. The field beyond is Pedlar field with lambing ewes let out to graze during daylight hours. A row of troughs for feeding meal can just be distinguished on the extreme left of the picture.1960.

the 2nd world war. His brother Bill however had been to France during the First World War.

Sixty years ago everybody knew everyone else in the village with the Sunday services at either chapel or church providing a focal point for people to have a change of dress from their working garb and have an opportunity to meet and have a chat with other folk that they perhaps otherwise wouldn't meet for weeks on end. Whilst the majority of folk were strictly church or chapel many would attend their chosen place of worship twice every Sunday, although they did join together to support each other's Harvest Festivals, chapel anniversaries, American teas and Garden Fetes, with the latter being an eagerly anticipated social highlight of the year. Nowadays village communities have completely changed, with many people using villages purely for dormitory accommodation, and in the process, destroying the close knit rural way of life that had previously endured for centuries.

Life in those days seemed to be uncomplicated with little of the envy so common place today.

Situated opposite Hill House Farm yard in Chapel Lane stood a small two up and two down mud and stud cottage with a red painted corrugated iron roof that came to within 7 feet of the ground and overhanging two tiny multi paned windows on either side of the front door. At some point in its history the roof of this house, in common with Mr and Mrs Humberstons house of a similar design, (mentioned elsewhere in this book), must have been thatched, and the Scrope estate who owned both properties must have considered that to reroof the cottages with metal sheeting would be a much cheaper option than the cost of re-thatching.

The front and only external door leading into the cottage opened onto a narrow passage with a door to the left that opened into the front or best room which was only used on a Sunday, whilst a door on the right led down a step into the kitchen and general living area. A fire constantly burned in the grate of the black range situated on the kitchens inside wall as it provided the only means of cooking and heating water. A large oven dominated one side of the range whilst a large chrome tap that supplied hot water from the back boiler was positioned on the other. All the water that was used in the house, including the water contained in the fireside supply tank for the back boiler, had to be carried in a metal bucket from a hand pump situated fifty yards away at the back of the farm yard. Little wonder that folk used water sparingly, so that everyone used the same water on the weekly bathnight in front of the fire.

Two easy chairs were drawn up on either side of the range, whilst set into the far wall a door led into a low ceilinged north facing pantry. On the opposite wall to the range was an assortment of uncomfortable straight backed chairs drawn up to an oil cloth covered table. The kitchen/living room was poorly illuminated by the single window which was situated immediately above an ancient brown chaise lange that provided what appeared to be the permanent residency for a couple of fat, tabby cats.

From the time my Grandfather bought Hill House Farm in 1920 the cottage was occupied by whoever was the current herdsman, during the 1940s the position was held by Ted Cartwright and his large family. He was a small wiry man who carried little surplus flesh, judging by the way the skin on his face was stretched like parchment over his under lying bone structure. It gave ample testament to a lifetime's hard manual work spent outside in all weathers. I remember he always used to wear his flat cap inclined at such an angle over his left ear that I used to marvel how he could possibly manage to prevent it falling off his head. Ted's job involved feeding the cattle at South View farmyard and preparing Lincoln Red bulls for shows and sales by halter breaking them so that they would lead, followed by washing and grooming them in order that they could be shown to best advantage.

When Mrs Cartwright was not washing, cooking or mending clothes for her large family she could be found cutting up small squares of material from garments that were passed repairing, and inserting them into the coarse weave of a brown hessian sack like material to make snip rugs that covered the floor.

The toilet comprised two wooden seats, side by side, in a small brick privy 40 yards away at the bottom of the garden next door to the pigsty.

Ted's Rhubarb grew alongside the back wall of the privy and produced fantastic crops of some of the best tasting Rhubarb in the district.

Every inch of the large garden was cultivated resulting in Ted being pretty well self sufficient in vegetables, with any trimmings and waste food being fed to his pig.

Mr & Mrs Parkinson were the last residents prior to the house being demolished in 1968 to make way for two modern bungalows that now completely fill the site.

Charles Kent had a small but very efficient dairy farm at Monks Farm on the Louth road adjacent to where the North Cockerington branch of Monks Dyke flows alongside part of the property before crossing the road. During the summer months the Kent family called at houses around the village selling tomatoes which they grew within a large wooden greenhouse in their garden. Their tomatoes in contrast to the vast majority of tomatoes that are now sold commercially were full of taste as they were grown in soil and only picked when they had fully ripened on the plant. Today's tomatoes are picked under ripe and grown in a soilless medium that's fed with a cocktail of liquid nutrients.

Fifty years ago hardly a day would pass without a visit from a farm trade rep selling anything from farm machinery to agricultural lime.Many reps however, such as Mr Crampton for example, from Grimsby, earned a living by selling a very narrow range of products which in his case was Rock Salt, that was used then, and still continues to this day to be used as an animal mineral. Mr Crampton was quite a thick set man who sported a large hearing aid in one ear, with a wire leading from it to a large battery pack cum amplifier that he had a distracting habit of constantly removing from his waistcoat pocket, before giving it a twiddle and then replacing it in his pocket once again. He always gave the impression of being a little unsure of himself as with a rather questioning look he would reply "Yiss" to any questions that we posed. He was either profoundly deaf, or he played on his disability using it as a very effective selling technique with any statement made to him invariable resulting in a puzzled frown as though in deep contemplation of a very serious response, then he would respond "eh". After several repeat performances and lots more "eh's", in exasperation we would place an order for a quarter of a ton so that we could get rid of him and continue with our work, at which point his hearing suddenly had a dramatic recovery as he announced,

"I'll bring you a ton and half next Monday morning."

There must have been quite a hefty profit margin because he had to compete with other reps selling a much wider range of animal minerals which also included rock salt, but of course that was tempered by the fact that there was a much greater number of small farms than is the case today, so there was plenty of scope for him to secure lots of very small orders as it would have been the exception to call on a farm that didn't carry livestock.

Battle Haywood and Bowers rep from Lincoln called for a sheep dip order whilst Osmond's from Grimsby offered a wide range of products based on fishmeal or cod liver oil. Sowerbys of Grimsby sold us hard dry slabs of high protein linseed and cotton cake which was a by-product of the oil extraction process. The seeds were pressed for their oil content and the residue was left in dry slabs rather like planks of wood. We passed these slabs of cake through a cake breaker that consisted of two intermeshing spiked rollers that broke the slabs into small lumps which could then be more easily incorporated into our home-grown ground cereals that we fed to the stock. At that time we purchased the majority of our blended cattle feeding stuffs from Barker and Lee Smith who had their mills in Lincoln, and were especially well known amongst their many farming clients for providing magnificent spreads of food at the summer shows, using Terrys of York as their caterers. Mr Bartlet was their extremely affable rep who visited my father for orders on a very regular basis. Seated comfortably in an easy chair in my parent's living room, sipping a cup of tea, and occasionally something stronger, he would light his pipe, at a time when the dangers of tobacco smoke were unrecognised, and set an example to other would be salesman by his easy manner coupled with total knowledge of his subject.

Some salesmen were much more aggressive in their delivery, whilst a few tended to be condescending and others just did not have confidence in the products they were selling. I remember one man, who was the rep for a well known seed company who had completely the wrong approach, resulting in him rarely selling anything to us. He was rather short in statue and overweight though always immaculately attired as he always sported a fresh flower in his buttonhole, but he had a rather pompous attitude. He always seemed to have a contemptuous look on his face as he stepped out of his car in the farm yard and enquired from any nearby farm workers if the boss was about. I met him several times whilst in my working clothes

Les Fidling reaping grass on one our grey "Fergie" tractors, late 50s.

Dave Fidling (Les`s father who was herdsman for the farm during the 1950s) holding one of our Lincoln Red bulls awarded Champion at Louth Bull Fair.

63

and did not appreciate his superior attitude when he considered that I and other farm workers were almost below his dignity to speak to. He never did discover that had his attitude been different he would have discovered that I was in fact one of the bosses.

Every machinery dealership at that time had sufficient reps to enable them to call on all the farms within their patch on a very regular basis, in order that they could at the very least have an opportunity to promote their franchised products.

Until the Lincolnshire Show settled on its permanent showground at Lincoln it travelled around the county for its annual 2 day show.

Farmers did their utmost to visit the show as it was an occasion for bills to be settled and orders placed for animal feeding stuffs, seed corn and agricultural machinery. Trade stands provided generous hospitality as they displayed the products they were selling.

CHAPTER 6
Schooldays

"See you at half term in November", was my father's parting words as he waved a hand through the wound down window of his pre war Austin 10, then disappeared with my mother by his side out of the entrance to De Aston Grammar School on September 6th 1948.

Apart from my stay in hospital this was the first time that I had lived away from home. I remember looking out of the car window as the car left home and gazing longingly up Stewton Road towards Conscience Hill, wondering when I would see the familiar sight once more.

I felt pretty wretched standing by the main entrance to the school alongside two wooden boxes that contained not quite all my worldly goods, but considering the trouble it had taken mother to amass the extensive list of clothing and bedding that the school had requested with the restrictions imposed by war time rationing coupons, it almost seemed like it.

Walter West the village carpenter had constructed a sturdy 18 inch square wooden box described as a Tuck Box with a padlocked hinged lid and painted in a light brown colour, where cakes sent from home, (as sweets were still rationed until I left school 5 years later), were stored along with any purely personal items.

I had a large trunk of the type seen in early silent cinema films, when native porters wearing little more than a loin cloth bear one as they struggle up the gangway on to a passenger liner. My trunk had probably seen that kind of service, as it had been purchased by my parents at a furniture sale in Louth. Following extensive renovation by Walt West it received a coat of very dark brown paint and became the depository for all my clothing and bedding.

Although Market Rasen was only 20 miles away, I seemed to be so cut off from home that to all intents and purposes it could just as easily have been 200 miles for all the difference it made. I was only a couple of weeks beyond my 11th birthday but was now embarking on 5 years of totally regimented life under headmaster Mr Horace Clews, where little

The 3 of us at Hill House farmyard 1951. Note the uncovered crewyard above. The building to the right of the ladder in the bottom photograph is the glasshouse.

Outside De Aston Grammar School 1951. L-R Edward "Ted" Reynolds, brother Bryan Arthur, self.

room was left for initiative as the principle requirement was to obey implicitly, and under no circumstances to question authority.

The 7 weeks to that first half term break seemed an eternity when the new boys were mercilessly bullied by the newly created prefects in the 6th form. Every minute of the day was strictly regulated from getting up in the morning to lights out in our large communal dormitory at 8 o\ clock at night. The harsh regime ensured that we made our beds in a strictly prescribed manner that had to pass daily inspection before we could come down for breakfast. When lessons ended in the afternoon at 3 45 pm and the day boys left to be bused home, the boarders had to change into running kit and run a 5 mile cross country course, after which we showered before sitting down to tea in the refectory. Prep commenced prompt at 6 pm in one of the classrooms under the tutelage of one of the masters and lasted until 7 30 when it was upstairs for a wash or twice weekly bath then bed and lights out at 8. The Sunday compulsory regime started for those who were confirmed with an early walk down to the parish church for the 8 am communion service. This was followed by breakfast, after which we had to write home and in order to confirm that we had actually written the letters, they were frequently read. Sunday life continued with matins alternating between the school hall and the parish church of St Thomas in Market Rasen when we all walked down in strictly regimented crocodile formation. Following lunch in the refectory, our next exercise was a 3 miles walk to Willingham Bridge and back where our names were ticked off a list ensuring that everyone completed the task. When tea was completed we had to attend evensong either in the hall or again on alternate Sundays in the parish church.

There were few joyous moments to break relief from this moral sapping regime though visits to Mrs Masons nearby tuck shop provided light relief over a small bottle of Vimto.

On Saturday afternoons following lessons in the morning we were allowed to walk into town provided that we were not taking part in organised team sports with other schools, but with very little money to spend and sweets still rationed it was all rather pointless although it did give us a brief respite from the place.

I distinctly remember, all these many years later walking down one of the school corridors soon after evening prep had finished and could not help overhearing two masters as they walked towards me enquiring the whereabouts of a certain boy who I had just passed. Trying to be helpful

I said "excuse me Sir I couldn't help overhearing you but I have just seen Morgan going into room 7."

The master turned to me and boxing me around the ears said,

"If I want you to speak to me boy I shall ask you".

His name was Mr Wilde, a maths teacher, and perhaps his attitude contributed to my intense dislike of the subject.

I soon made good friends with Edward (Ted) Reynolds from Grimsby, whose father was a partner in the family fish merchants on Grimsby Docks. Both of his parents also ran a dance school at the Theatre Royal in Cleethorpes, where in addition to teaching dancing, they trained a leading formation dance team in the 1940s and 50s. In spite of coming from totally different backgrounds we had a very good rapport with each other that led to a very close friendship throughout the 5 years I was at De Aston resulting in us spending part of each school holiday at each other's home. Ted stayed on into the 6th form when I left school just short of my 16th birthday in July 1953, when inevitably we both went our separate ways as I made a new circle of friends within the Young Farmers Club movement and he later joined the personnel division of Courtaulds, on the Humber bank, just west of Grimsby (upon leaving school). It was probably unsurprising that having artistic parents he would be fond of music, so it was no surprise to see pictures and articles in the Grimsby Evening Telegraph of Edward Reynolds playing clarinet in his High Society jazz band.

Some years later during the 1970s Pat, my wife and I made contact once again with Ted when we met socially at each other's home and reminisced over our experiences at De Aston.

We were therefore extremely saddened to learn from a front page article in the Grimsby Evening Telegraph in February 1987 that Ted had taken his own life. Glowing tributes were paid to him at his funeral service in St James church in Grimsby when friends described his brilliance as a musician and how his very sensitive nature made it difficult for him to cope with the stresses of heading Courtaulds large personnel department.

I suppose that with reflection my time at school was a period when I developed trading skills because 9d a week pocket money did not finance many purchases at Mrs. Mason's tuck shop, nor the ability to do little other than window shop in the town.

At that time the principle everyday activity during the mid morning break and after lunch was completed, revolved around games of marbles, when any bare patch of the sandy soil in the school grounds became a well trodden marble pitch, where the games objective was to be first to get your marble into a grubby hole and thus win all of your opponent's marbles. I got quite good at this game and regularly won enabling me to sell off my winning marbles with the more colourful glass ones commanding a higher price.

I discovered that stamp collecting was another good revenue earner as most boys then collected stamps in much the same way as today's boys collect footballer's cards. Stamp selling companies used to advertise what were optimistically described as "Stamp Approvals" in comics such as The Eagle and Champion. They might for example offer one hundred free stamps as an inducement to get a potential customer to receive their booklets of individually priced stamps, hoping that having got their stamps into a collectors hands a sale would invariably follow.

I quickly latched on to the demand for stamps from the seemingly affluent dayboys, and produced my own books comprising stamps that I had received free.

I found that at the end of term I could manage to take home all of my accumulated pocket money that was doled out on a weekly basis, and yet still have money to spend in Mrs Masons tuck shop where I remember that one of her best selling lines were bags of broken Smiths crisps costing 1d each.

Reflecting back on those days there is little doubt that the boarding school environment enabled me to mix with other boys from a very wide spectrum of differing backgrounds from many parts of the country. Some of the boy's parents were in the armed services enabling them to stir my imagination, relating about what seemed to me, to be exotic places overseas that I could only read about in books. I joined several school societies that organised trips to places as diverse as a coal mine at Thorne and my first visit to London to see the 1951 Festival of Britain.

Coming from a farming family in east Lincolnshire I had never travelled very far, largely as a consequence of war time restrictions but also because of my parent's seasonal farming commitments. For example we could never go away for a family holiday during the long summer school holidays because of harvest on the farm, and of course a holiday at Easter time was similarly out of the question as cattle were being turned out and required droving to outlying fields. Likewise at Christmas it was equally impossible to get away because mother dressed and prepared what seemed like hundreds of Christmas poultry.

It would be fair to say that I did not enjoy my five years at boarding school and could not wait till I returned home for the holiday periods because all I ever wanted to do was be involved in farming and growing things.

There's an oft repeated saying, that claims the reason that farmers persist in pursuing a life in farming with long unsociable hours and poor remuneration is, that it must be in the blood, whatever that's supposed to mean. In reality I suspect that the real reason has much more to do with the fact that the children of farming families have never known anything different to life on a farm. Very few occupations or professions have their work all about them when they open the back door of their house. What makes farming both interesting and challenging and sometimes quite frustrating is that every day is different and certainly no two years are alike, when decisions have to be constantly revised in response to differing weather conditions and changing markets.

Looking at my time at boarding school from the historical perspective of fifty seven years I recognise that of course there were benefits of which independence and self reliance was paramount. I think that had I not been in that environment at such an early age I would not have had the confidence to embark on many of the projects that I participated in within a few years of leaving school.

CHAPTER 7
Mid Marsh Young Farmers Club

"Here's an invitation for Ralph to attend Mid Marsh Young Farmers Club at 7.30 pm on the 3rd Friday in September," remarked Nancy Speed, a milk analyst with the Milk Marketing Board, to my father at Louth Cattle Market, on learning that I would shortly be joining the family farm as I was about to leave school.

That first meeting in September 1953 opened the door to 10 of the most enjoyable and satisfying years of my life when thanks to the YFC movement I had the opportunity to learn new skills and reach the highest office within the county organisation, in addition to representing the United Kingdom as I quite literally travelled around the world.

During that very first meeting participants for the inter club autumn rally were being selected. A voice from the back of the room proposed that Ralph Needham could judge sheep, presumably basing his nomination on the premise that as his father had sheep on the farm he must know something about them, thus making him highly qualified to judge them. Little did the proposer realise that sheep husbandry did not figure on the De Aston school curriculum, and furthermore, my interest in the animals during school holidays was rather prejudiced against them, as it usually involved droving a flock of the scatty creatures to various fields on the farm when I would have much preferred to be doing lots of other things. In the competition I was expected to place four fat lambs in order of merit as butcher's animals, but then I learned to my utter horror that I would have to explain in a speech lasting two minutes my reasons for doing so to the overall master judge. He would quickly realise that I knew very little about what I was describing, especially as he would be an expert on the finer points of sheep judging, and not be someone who would appreciate hearing a load of waffle from a complete novice. I was given a crash course on which points should be given the greater preference, but was soon confused with what to me was a multitude of completely new terminology. Adding to my confusion I couldn't remember whether it was better for an ideal butchers lamb to have a thinner dock, indicating that the lamb would not be too fat. Or should it have a fat dock which would mean it had a superior eye muscle? (The dock is the lambs tail which is a good measure of the animals fatness when feeling for the amount of fat cover surrounding the bony vertebrae). Then what was that about spring of rib, and how did the loin fit in? Was the leg of lamb the front or the back leg?

I did not do very well in that very first competition but over the years I did improve and went on to generally win eventually representing the county, and after leaving the YFC at the age of 25 I became the county coach. I soon made some very good friends as I whole heartedly participated in a wide spectrum of YFC activities from social events in village halls around the district, to agriculturally related factory visits, or attending demonstrations and listening to some very interesting speakers. At the age of 17 I passed my driving test and was able to take over the farm Land Rover which gave me a great deal more independence as it enabled me to travel where and when I wanted to go. Within two years I was elected club vice chairman and the following year chairman when I was supported by an enthusiastic team of extremely capable officers. We arranged tuition, and then booked examiners in Proficiency tests for a wide diversity of farm crafts and skills ranging from such subjects as Tractor Maintenance to Poultry Plucking and Trussing. For example I particularly remember starting a week's Hedge Laying course sometimes

Hedge laying course at Great Carlton in January 1958 L-R   Roger Taylor, Self, Rowland Kipling, Mr Johnson the instructor, Sam Scamen.

72

Self taking part in a sheep shearing competition at Hainton show 1955. Brother Arthur and his friend from De Aston, Robert Tasker are 2nd and 3rd right.

Self as Mid Marsh club chairman in 1958 holding the County Eficiency cup for the most efficient YFC in the county. Backrow - Roger Taylor, Muriel Robinson, Janice Hewerdine, Bryan Needham (brother) Barbara Odlin, Bryan Hewerdine, Elizabeth Shucksmith, John Needham.
Front Row Ann Stubbs nee Brown, Mararet Swan nee West, Self, Tom Heys, Cyril Walker president.

73

called Plashing in late January 1957. Six of us assembled, one particularly cold winter Monday morning, in a field at Great Carlton, alongside an over- grown hawthorn hedge to commence four days of tutelage by Mr. Johnson, an expert Plasher, who had travelled over from Wragby. Mr. Johnson had come well prepared for cold weather, because his stocky frame was cloaked for the duration of the week by an all encompassing heavy, black, ex police coat. With the collar turned up at the neck, it provided an almost seamless link with a grey Homburg hat pulled firmly down over his ears to successfully defy the worst of the bitter January weather. The north easterly wind increased in strength and whipped mercilessly through the spartan hedge. I, along with my five other YFC colleagues, Don Brader, Bryan Hewerdine, Roland Kipling, Sam Scamen and Roger Taylor were beginning to regret embarking on this crazy course in freezing weather on the windswept Lincolnshire Marsh in January. Snowflakes started to filter from a leaden sky through the leafless branches of the hawthorn hedge. Mr Johnson gathered us around him. After several deep draws on the stem of his briar pipe, that seemed to be permanently clenched between his teeth, he went on to demonstrate from within a haze of white smoke how a hedge should be plashed concluding with the words, *"You know the best part of this job is that you'll get two warms"*. *"How do you make that out"*, Don questioned between chattering teeth. *"First you get warm chopping and then you will get another warm as you burn the brash."* Mr Johnson declared with a wide grin on his face. *"You must partially chop the stem with your cleavers,"* he continued, grasping a particularly spiny hawthorn stem with his gloved left hand, as he demonstrated the chopping technique with the cleaver held in his right hand. *"Chop about nine inches above ground level, being extremely careful not to completely sever the stem, and then bend it over making sure that you lay it in the same direction as all the other stems that you have plashed. The object of the exercise"*, he pointed out, *"Is to create a solid stock proof hedge from a hedge that has been neglected and grown upwards resulting in it losing its bottom."*

He emphasised that we should all be particularly careful using our razor sharp twenty inch cleavers as it was extremely easy to remove a thumb. Shaking with cold in the bitter north easterly wind we wielded our cleavers and soon accumulated a sizeable pile of brash. Mr Johnson made occasional forays to inspect our progress before retreating out of the wind to the lee of a stout tree stump where he passed the time in a haze of white smoke from his trusty pipe, indicating that he had come

YFC spring rally at South View Farm South Cockerington May 1960. Note on top left of bottom picture the pipe that crossed the road to convey grain from the old granary to a new grain store to the pictures right.

well prepared with a good supply of tobacco. Before long he announced, "I think we will we take a break in the Wagon and Horses", (the local pub in nearby South Reston) and have some "technical training", after which we'll come back and burn the brash whilst we eat our lunch".

The afternoon seemed to pass much quicker as we felt much warmer in front of a blazing fire in spite of a light dusting of snow covering the frozen ground. As the week progressed the new hedge looked quite professional with a line of freshly sawn stakes pinning the new hedge in a straight line. On the Friday morning we were each set a test to see how proficient we were in hedge laying when we each had 2 hours to plash 25 yards of hedge in front of an examiner, which we all happily passed.

This course was indicative of so many that were undertaken at the time providing members with new skills and enjoyable comradeship. In our case the YFC more than lived up to its motto of Good Farmers, Good Citizens, and Good Countrymen. Weekly meetings were held every Friday night in Great Carlton village hall, commencing with a business meeting followed by a talk or demonstration by an invited speaker. A wide range of subjects, of not only general interest but also particular topics to cater for both male and female members were covered.

I learned valuable lessons, in not only being able to properly conduct a meeting but also to be uninhibited by speaking in public. The 7 years from 1953 to 1960 passed incredibly quickly with a seemingly endless variety of YFC activities ranging from proficiency tests to public speaking competitions in addition to the more practical farming related competitions held at both the spring and autumn rallies, when our club competed against other clubs in the county. There were a wide range of social events such as balls and dances along with summer time bus trips to the seaside at Scarborough or Great Yarmouth. I got my first taste for travel in May 1957 when I joined the county federation under the leadership of county organiser Sybil Raper for a two week holiday by rail and sea to visit Denmark and Sweden that cost the princely sum of £22. To travel abroad in those days before the advent of widespread air travel was quite an adventure when very few people other than armed service personnel had been outside of the United Kingdom. The furthest that most people had generally travelled was London. Following an overnight ferry crossing from Harwich we caught the Scandinavian express train at the Hook of Holland that took us across war torn northern Europe to Lubeck on the Baltic. I saw the results of the allied bombing missions which I vividly recalled forming up in formations over the Louth area little over 12 years earlier. Parts of Hamburg that the train passed through, had been totally flattened, but was now relieved by the surreal appearance of thousands of pear trees in virginal white blossom, demonstrating graphically that despite the total ravages of war nature can regenerate itself in pristine clarity. The trip was a great experience introducing me to unfamiliar countries, languages and food. This wetted my appetite in more ways than one to join the trip the following year when northern Spain and Majorca would be visited. In May 1958 we once again travelled by train, but on this occasion across France to the resort of Tossa del Mar on the Costa Brava in Northern Spain. It was still a sleepy fishing village with sand covered alleys that served as roads between the fishermen's houses and the fairly basic lodgings that we stayed in. Our organiser managed to arrange transport for us on an ex military DC3 across to Majorca for a day trip, enabling most of to us to fly for the very first time. I realised that I wanted to do much more travelling and became aware of the International Exchange scholarships that the YFC organised. I learned that there were several places awarded on a regional basis for short stays of 7 to 14 days to some European countries. Much longer three month trips awarded to 6 people who were selected from all of the UK regions to travel to Ontario in Canada, and another 6 to visit two US states. Finally 6 people would be selected for 6 months in Australia, and a further 2 people selected for 2 places to take 9 months travelling around the world spending a month in Australia and 6 months in New Zealand. By 1959 I reasoned that I had benefitted so much, and in so many ways by my 6 years in the Young Farmers Club movement that I felt it was worth an attempt to apply for an overseas exchange visit. In all seriousness I didn't really rate my chances very highly, as I knew that there would be enormous competition from members all over the country.

With the knowledge that it would require all my available spare time gaining information on the relevant countries history, geography and economy for at least a year I might as well try for the most difficult trip of Australia and New Zealand on the basis that I would travel the furthest and hopefully see the most. I made my initial application in summer 1959 and successfully passed my county interview progressing on to the East Midlands interviews, were I met all of the other county winners and was selected to represent the East Midland area at the National Finals in London in January 1960. I achieved the runner up position.

I resolved that having got so far I would repeat the exercise during the 1960/61 winter. I was successful in being awarded one of the two coveted places in February 1961, along with Alan Mather from North Devon. Our ship the 28000 ton P&O Himalaya departed Tilbury docks on May 5th 1961 with an emotional send off. Many people aboard were emigrating to an unknown future on the far side of the earth with the prospect that they may never see members of their family again.

The voyage took us to Gibraltar then across to Athens as we picked up more passengers, before transiting the Suez canal and calling at Aden, where I purchased a slide projector and 25 rolls of 36 exposure slide film. Our next port of call was Colombo on May 21st followed 7 days later by Perth in Western Australia were we left two of the 6 visiting Australia. We left the other two pairs in Adelaide and Melbourne, whilst Alan and I continued on to Sydney where we parted company for the next two weeks.

Alan went to the west of New South Wales as I caught an overnight sleeper travelling north to Glen Innes up on the Queensland border. Highlights of my time in Northern New South Wales included riding a horse bareback at full gallop and shooting Kangaroos from the back of a ten ton lorry travelling at 40mph over native bush country. By the end of June both Alan and I arrived in Auckland to start our six month tour of New Zealand following a rough three day passage over the Tasman Sea on board the SS Wanganella. We travelled together down to Wellington and caught the overnight ferry to Cristchurch were we parted company, hoping to meet up again three months later in Wellington, on September 15th.

I was issued with a sizeable wad of travel vouchers for a whole range of transportation that would take me by air, train, bus and ship for the following three months journeys around the South Island. The Bank of New Zealand sponsored all my travelling in New Zealand.

The 22nd June 1961 dawned a bright clear crisp winter's day with the magnificent panorama of the white snow capped Southern Alps standing out in sharp relief in the crystal clear air. Armed with my first ticket at Christchurch station I said to a railway official, *"Which platform does the train to Waimate leave from"* pronouncing it Way mate. The man scratched his head exclaiming that *"there was nowhere in the South Island by that name possibly it was somewhere in the North Island"*. Becoming slightly worried that I had been issued with wrong tickets I showed him my ticket when his face beamed with a mixture of bemused condescension and incredulity that anyone could be so stupid, saying as he turned away, "Why matee, platform 3". The next three months revolved around staying with farming families in their homes and observing how they lived, when I was not only shown around their farms but also taken on visits to their neighbour's farms, in addition to seeing some of the

Drilling Oats on Malcolm Guys farm near Levin, North Island, New Zealand Sept 1961. Malcolm represented New Zealand in USA two years later.

countries spectacular mountain scenery. Throughout my time in both Australia and later in New Zealand my bulky projector accompanied me on my travels when I used it to illustrate scores of talks by showing slides that I had taken with me. Host families were exceptionally generous, giving so freely of their time, and in all cases making me so welcome. They were particularly fascinated by my slides of Lincolnshire and village life at home, along with views of market towns such as Louth and Alford, as most folk I stayed with were either second or third generation immigrants who had heard so many stories about Britain from parents or grandparents and still referred to England as the "old country".

England in the 1960s seemed an awful long way from New Zealand it took a month to travel there by ship as reliable air services were still in their infancy.

During those three winter months notable highlights included visits to scores of farms and seeing some magnificent stock in some very difficult wild country. I flew in a small aircraft among the razor edged peaks of the Southern Alps, and on another occasion flew on a rare sunny winter's morning to Milford Sound, some years before the Homer Tunnel had

A kiwi approach to digging a ditch with dynamite at a forage demonstration I attended near Hamilton NZ.

been constructed. I enjoyed a lobster lunch as I gazed at the stunning Mitre Peake rising 8000 feet above the fiord. I saw the Fox and Franze Joseph glaciers on the West Coast, and went skiing on Coronet Peak were the only facilities comprised two huts and a rope ski lift. During my stay on the West Coast near Hokatika, I was invited one day to accompany a stock buyer on a buying mission to a remote ranch 100 miles to the south along gravel roads and washed out river beds. As we ate our lunch in a very basic beer house, that served the isolated community, the publican said that he had been listening to the BBC world service on his short wave radio, but due to the remote location, quite literally on the far side of the earth, he could only pick up odd words between the static. Bearing in mind that this was a full year before the Cuban missile crisis reached its climax, his statements were alarming when he said,

"There's no point in you boys going back as I've heard Russia,- nuclear bombs,- America, holocaust, world war. You had better spend your last days here with us". Thankfully my driver took a more pragmatic view as we made a very reflective three hour journey back to Hokatika. Issued with another wedge of tickets, I commenced the next three months part of my journey in Wellington, travelling throughout the North Island when I marvelled at the intensive dairy farms in Waikato and the awe inspiring geo thermal areas around Rotorua. I stayed with the Jenkins family on their intensive Jersey dairy farm in the lee of snow capped Mount Egmont rising Fuji like from the flat plain of Taranaki. In the King Country, Cyril Perry was my host on his incredibly steep sheep and cattle farm that was racked almost nightly by earth tremors. I witnessed at first hand New Zealanders unconventional approach to tackling problems illustrated by such examples as digging a new ditch with a box of dynamite, or breaking in virgin natural bush, pulling a ten ton solid filled roller with knives fitted longitudinally down a hillside gradient of one in one.

I climbed volcanic Mount Ruapehu and was taken up to Russell in the Bay of Islands and then through the giant Kauri forests in Northland. All too soon the tour was over and I flew down to Christchurch spending a week with Fred and Eva Martin, who were distant relations living in Timaru. Flying north once more I was reunited with Alan Mather again as we boarded the New Zealand Shipping Company's 17000 ton RMS Ruahine, carrying frozen lamb and dairy produce along with 250 passengers, on the four and a half week voyage back to the UK.

Sailing across the Pacific Ocean ensured that we had circum navigated the globe as the ship broke its voyage calling at the then, rather remote and exotic isle of Tahiti. The journey was completed as we transited the remarkable locks of the Panama Canal, and then called at glitzy Fort Lauderdale in Florida, before a particularly stormy crossing over the North Atlantic landing, at a cold Southampton, on January 13th 1962.

Over the course of the next two years I delivered in excess of 100 talks, illustrated by slides that I had taken on my travels, to YFCs throughout Lincolnshire and Nottinghamshire as well as other organisations, as diverse as Women's Institutes and Lindsey County Council.

It was following my talk to members of Lindsey County Council that the rest of my life could so easily have turned in a completely different direction. Lieutenant Colonel Sir Weston Cracroft Armcotes the Councils chairman had invited me to address the councillors on my experiences in New Zealand, a country, which in those days very few people knew much about, let alone had visited, due to its inaccessibility on the far side of the earth. After publicly thanking me for my illustrated talk he came over to me and said, "I own a sizable farm in New Zealand's south island at present run by a manager. I was most impressed with your knowledge

Self panning for gold near Hokitika on the west coast of the South Island.

and as my manager is retiring shortly wonder if you would consent to operate the farm for me". I was extremely flattered by his invitation, and said that I would give it serious consideration and notify him of my decision over the next few days.

My parents were probably with some justification totally opposed to the idea as they thought that they would only very rarely see me again as the age of worldwide jet travel still lay some years in the future. In the final analysis I decided against it though I have to say that it was a very difficult decision, as I reasoned that although I was very much the junior partner in the family farm at home, it was probably better to stay with the devil that I knew, than the one, that in spite of looking attractive, might not live up to expectations.

My 8 months of travelling was a fantastic experience as it made me very self reliant and not to suffer fools gladly. It broadened my outlook on life enabling me to look at world events from a much more rounded perspective. Above all it gave me the confidence to be undaunted as I faced any challenge and attempted new projects, even to the extent of writing this book forty-six years later. My active YFC involvement ended in 1966 following two years as county vice chair and finally two years as county chairman.

CHAPTER 8
My Early Farming Years

I joined our family farming company when I left school in the summer of 1953, never having remotely considered any career other than farming.

The family farm had been run as a partnership until 1947 when for taxation reasons my father and uncle who up to that time had been running the business as a partnership were advised by our accountant to form a limited company with the shares equally divided between my father who specialised in the pedigree livestock side of the business and his brother Jack who looked after the arable side. Jack's son John had entered the business 7 years earlier than me, and followed his father's interest in machinery and the production of arable crops. Given my father's position as one the country's leading pedigree cattle breeders it was perhaps hardly surprising that he should encourage me to follow him and specialize in livestock breeding.

It was therefore quite natural that after a couple of years on the farm that he should pass responsibility for looking after the 330 commercial ewe flock over to me. I spent long hours during the early spring lambing the ewes, making sure that lambs were not mismatched, in itself a difficult task when sometimes two or three ewes would lamb in the same spot. The problem then arose in matching the correct lambs to the right mothers as sometimes ewes would accept a wrong lamb initially, only to reject it later and then the correct mother would also reject it as it had acquired a fresh smell.

During the day, the ewes were turned out to graze in Pedlar field, which until it was under drained and ploughed in 1972 was a permanent grass field. Its original highland rig and furrow contours had been created in the mid 19th century following the installation of half moon clay pipes called sluffs into hand dug land drains with the excavated soil forming the typical corrugated effect.

The ewes were brought into a temporary fold each night that was constructed every lambing season around the old granary. Individual pens for newly lambed ewes were made of sheep hurdles cloaked in wheat straw and erected in a line to the rear of the wagon house that lay under the granary.

The majority of ewes that lambed during the day time seemed to take a perverse delight in selecting the top of the field to have their young, which unfortunately was the furthest point from the gate leading out of the field in the bottom corner. About every couple of hours I walked around the field looking for any ewes that had either lambed or were in the process of giving birth. If a ewe had lambed I had to quickly get the shivering newborn lambs down to the yard and into the shelter of one of the pens that were erected in various buildings around the yard. One of the most frustrating parts of the job that seemed to occur on a pretty regular basis was actually getting the ewe and her new born lambs out of the field and into the yard. After sloshing across the length of the field with my feet slipping and sliding in water filled sheep hoof marks I gripped the front legs of a couple of wet struggling lambs, whilst at the same time making a passable imitation of the lambs "maying" to encourage the mother to follow me. On reaching the gate fairly successfully the ewe would suddenly about turn and race headlong up to the top of the field again to the spot that she had lambed. By this time the wet newborn lambs were shivering uncontrollably and needed to be in the protection of the warm pens in the yard where they could dry off and have their first drink of milk. The exercise had to be repeated until such time as the new mother was ensconced with her new family in an individual pen, and given a fresh mangle to eat. Not all lambs would readily suck so the ewe had to be turned over in order that I could sit on her side, and by placing a teat in the lamb's mouth get it to suck the first drops of milk down its throat. I dealt with all of the seasonal tasks, which included dagging, (clipping off the wool matted with faeces around the animals back end), prior to washing. A little later in the season under the granary at Hill House Farm where the temporary lambing pens had been erected, I caught the sheep for Arthur Bentons clipping gang who worked on a raised platform consisted of the boarded body of a demolished trailers to shear the sheep.

Once the clippers had rolled a fleece into a tight bundle, I carried it up the stairs to the granary above them and packed it along with about 30 other fleeces into a wool sheet that rather resembled a 10 foot long by 5 foot high hessian envelope. The giant wool bag, called a wool sheet was suspended by a rope attached to its two top corners from an overhead beam which enabled me to pack the fleeces inside. I had to continually climb into the bag and squash the springy wool down with my feet until the bag was completely full. I then closed the wide neck of the envelope by pinning the edges together with a number of pointed hardwood pegs. Using an 8 inch sack needle threaded with a special waxed string I finally sewed both sides of the sheet securely together.

In 1955 the farms area expanded to about 850 acres following the purchase of the 170 acres Scupholme House Farm on the way to South Somercotes when we inherited along with the farm another three farm workers to add to the 8 who were already being employing at that time.

In 1961 the farm employed13 full time workers, but over the next 20 years 4 of the men who had either retired or moved on were not replaced as more sophisticated labour saving machinery was introduced on to the farm.

One of my father's daily tasks during the winter months was to walk through all the housed cattle at our various yards, and inspect them in much the same way that he would have looked at them during the summer months, but on these occasions he would liaise with garthmen whose full time winter time job was to bed and feed them. When the animals were out at grass he shepherded them every day in a pony and trap and then in later years inspected them from the seat of a Landrover. By 1970 both my father who was then approaching 70 with Jack three years older had virtually retired from active farming but never the less still retained a keen interest in the farm by driving around the farm during the summer months. From the mid sixties I assumed full responsibility from my father for dealing with all the paperwork involved with the pedigree recording of our Lincoln Red herd, as I was now responsible for selling all of the pedigree cattle. Forty years ago each small bale of feed and bedding had to be carried into the crew by hand, which was not only hard work but an extremely labour intensive. Today it's all done mechanically, our JCB fork lift effortlessly lifts and conveys two big round bales of straw at a time, (each one might weigh as much as 250 kgs or 5 cwt, equivalent to 30 of the small rectangular bales) into a crew for bedding, and with a few shakes of the powerful grab distribute straw all over the crew in just a few minutes. I can't help reflecting on the sheer volume of effort that used to be employed in handling these small bales, from bringing the bales in from the field, and then stacking them by hand into the furthest reaches of the Dutch barns. So many farm tasks at that time, quite literally relied on man power, so that one can readily understand how such a large labour force was gainfully employed even though the introduction of machines were a big improvement on what went before.

A good example of this was a mechanised Bamford hedge cutter that we bought in the late 50s, to replace cutting hedges by hand with a hedge knife commonly known as a slasher. The new machine comprised a 30 feet long by 6 inch diameter metal tube that was braced for rigidity, and mounted on a pivot positioned centrally above the bonnet on one of our grey Ferguson tractors. At one end of the tube a variable geometry, 5 foot reaper knife with a reciprocating blade could be positioned either at right angles to the tube for cutting the hedge side or positioned straight out for cutting the top of the hedge. A 10 hp Petter petrol engine providing motive power for the knife was mounted 30 feet away at the opposite end of the tube. A 'v' belt connected the engine to the knife, whilst a rope attached to a heavy metal weight within the tube could alter the balance by pulling the weight in either direction. Hedging was carried out by means of one man pushing a handle attached to the knife end of the tube against the hedge to be cut, whilst the other man drove the tractor forward parallel to the hedge row. Other men followed on behind with hand forks to collect the clippings from both the top and the side of the hedge. Today of course the operation is carried out by one man using a hydraulic flail mower that leaves the pulverised clippings in situ, returning the nutrients back to the soil for grubs and insects, thus providing feed for birds and small mammals.

It's easy to see, from the historical perspective of over 40 years, why such a large labour force was required compared to the minimal numbers employed on today's farms. Up to the end of the 1960s, when we dispersed our commercial sheep flock, we grew about 25 acres of mangolds and swedes to feed both them and cattle during the early spring. In the days before the invention of mono germ seed and modern beet drills, the seed was sown by an ancient, horse drawn, root drill that had been adapted to fit on the three point linkage of one of our grey Fergies. Whilst it measured out the low seed rate far more precisely than could ever be achieved by a conventional grain drill, inevitably it resulted in having a much too high plant population. By the end of May the seedlings had grown sufficiently large to allow a gang of 5 or 6 men armed with hoes to "chop out" about half an acre each, during an 8 hour day, spacing the clumps of plants roughly a foot apart. Three weeks later the operation had to be repeated when the clumps were reduced to one plant, (singled), retaining the best one in order that it could reach optimum size. Throughout the summer

Singling Mangolds in Mill Hill 1956 L-R Walter Evison, Reg Vickers, George Snowdon, Dave Fiddling, Les Fiddling, Lewis Parkinson.
Photo courtesy Mrs M Bathurst.

the growing plants had to be kept free of weeds, either by hand hoeing or using a two man mechanical hoe, mounted behind a tractor.

In early November up to 6 men were employed for a week pulling the roots (mangolds, turnips and swedes) and cutting off the green tops, when some of the larger specimens could weigh as much as 40 lbs.

The mangles had a variety of different colours ranging from white through yellow to dark red and pretty well all shades in between, though I suspect they all tasted similar to the sheep. The roots were stabbed with a fork then thrown into a trailer to be transported to the yard where they were heaped into a clamp about 10 feet high. Dyke reeds were mown with a scythe from the Marsh ditches and then placed over the clamp for frost protection. Later during the winter the roots were removed from the clamp and fed to the sheep when grass was in short supply.

Fencing was another heavy drain on labour, usually providing work for a two man team for several weeks during the winter months, as fences around permanent grass fields required annual maintenance. Towards the end of summer when grass was either getting in short supply or was past its tender best, cattle had a habit of reaching over fences and sometimes breaking them down, as they attempted to curl their long tongues around tender morsels of hedge. Short term grass and clover leys were rotated around the farm which entailed erecting a stock proof fence, consisting of squared pig netting topped with a strand of barbed wire around the unfenced fields. As the Monks Dyke watering system was now obsolete, a temporary water supply had to be introduced that involved rolling out black alkethene piping to fields, some of which could be more than a mile away from the farmyard's main water supply.

Until the end of the 1960s we used two, David Brown, steel tracked, 50 hp crawlers, that each towed a two furrow Ransome duo track plough. In the days before reversible ploughs, each field had to be marked out, each year, by a man who either walked, or in later years rode on another tractor holding a pre determined length of baler twine, with the plough man holding the other end as he made a "scrawl" with his back furrow.

The first round was only 20 yards from the outside of the field in order that the plough man would be left with a uniform distance at the finish. Subsequent lengths of string were much longer, often up to 60 or 70 yards, until such time as the middle was reached. Once the field was ploughed by travelling round and round from the middle to the outside,

Aerial photograph showing the effect of round hand ploughing.

the corners were ploughed to complete the process. The results of ploughing field's round hand can still be seen to this day by examining aerial photographs of uncropped land. Because the tractor only pulled two furrows, albeit ones up to 14 inches deep, ploughing was rarely finished by Christmas, when the ploughing crawler frequently required a tow by the other crawler to complete the last more difficult fields as the wet clay soils became incredibly slippery offering little purchase to the steel tracks. The same two crawlers were used for all cultivation work also pulling sets of heavy harrows to cultivate the soil in preparation for either spring or autumn cereals.

Over the years, I spent many unpleasant hours humping these extremely heavy harrows, along with the stretcher that pulled them, on and off a low loader as I helped move them from field to field.

I remember that the iron frames always seemed to be icy cold and were usually coated with sticky mud. The only effective way of carrying these 14 stones (90 kgs) monsters single handed, was by standing the harrow on its end with the tines looking away, then hooking one shoulder under the top bar and hope you didn't slip on the muddy ground as you walked across to the low loader.

Lewis Parkinson by one of the farms two David Brown 50hp crawlers. Note the home built cab and the trailed Ransomes 2 furrow Duotrac plough. Photo courtesy of Mrs M Bathurst.

A whole raft of grants and subsidies were introduced by the government after the Second World War to channel investment into modern buildings in order that the country could produce more of its food at home following the wartime experience of shortages when Britain was nearly starved into submission. Many of the old wooden boarded farm buildings that had been erected more than a century earlier, were starting to decay and were at the end of their useful lives. Roofs where rock lattes had rotted, allowed the clay pan tiles to slip or rusty corrugated iron roofing sheets fell to the ground causing rain water to inflict even more damage to the woodwork. An incredible amount of building and drainage investment was carried out during the 60s and early 70s that soaked up even more labour as we also demolished many of the low, brick, Victorian farm buildings that had become impractical for tractors to enter, and replaced them with modern, steel, clear span industrial type buildings with corrugated fibre cement roofs and concrete floors. Long hours were spent shoveling sand and gravel into the mouth of an ancient petrol engined, pre war cement mixer. It mixed all the cement for building the hollow, concrete block walls, and the concrete for the floors, until the introduction of ready mixed concrete relieved us of the latter operation. Over the years we must have laid a few thousand 9 inch square by 18 inch long concrete blocks that formed the walls of many of the new buildings. At fairly regular intervals we took a couple of our petrol/ paraffin and later diesel grey Ferguson tractors with 3 ton trailers, on what at that time seemed a major drive on the 10 or so miles to a concrete block manufacturer in Marshchapel, to collect 120 blocks at a time. In later years they were produced at the back of the Scunthorpe Builders yard almost opposite today's Priory hotel in Louths Eastgate. We didn't have the luxury of heated cabs or mudguards on those early tractors, so we had to rely on thick, army, great coats to keep warm. We placed a folded corn sack over our knees to prevent water spray from the wheels landing in our laps. Because of the tractors small back wheels and resultant limited ground clearance under the back axle, it was impractical to mount a hitch there, which of course would have been the most sensible towing position to give the tractor stability. Consequently trailers were attached to the swinging drawbar held on the three point linkage, resulting in the trailers weight being carried too far back. With little weight on the front wheels of the tractor, (no provision for front weights at that time), the driver had to constantly assist his steering by use of the two independent back brakes. Nowhere was this more challenging than towing a trailer full of sand and gravel up the steep

Hand gripping in the 1950s Photo courtesy of Mr Dance.

hill from the quarry at Welton le Wold to the Lincoln road, when the front wheels of the tractor would be clear of the road surface most of the way up the hill.

As bulk grain, handling systems replaced the hard labour of handling of sacks,we had to rapidly adapt our buildings by building new grain stores to reflect the much greater capacity coming from the second generation of combine harvesters. Initially existing buildings were converted by constructing 20 to 30 ton metal bins out of metal sheets to form panels. Grain was blown into these bins by means of a pneumatic blower, but emptying them was an altogether different story as practically all of the grain had to be shovelled by hand to a discharge outlet on one side. Later improvements saw the grain stored on the floor, in a similar manner to that found today, with drying or aeration carried out by means of metal, perforated, air ducts laid over the concrete floor leading to a drying tunnel powered by an electric fan. We built our first grain drying and storage system in 1960 at South View Farm, situated where Lavender Cottage now stands. We constructed the building ourselves using concrete blocks. It stood aproximately 20 feet high and held two rows of Simplex aerated, 25 ton bins. These bins were filled by means of a bucket type elevator from a discharge pit and an overhead conveyor, whilst emptying was carried out by an underground conveyer moving the grain to the same elevator that was used for filling the bins, but this time with the outlet swivelled in the other direction in order that bulk lorries could be loaded.

New covered crew yards were erected at all of the cattle yards to replace old partially open air yards, that were not only difficult to keep clean but were also a challenge to clean out using tractors with fore end loaders.

During the space of 15 years, Vickers land drainage contractors from Saltfleetby using specialist drainage machines, drained most of the arable fields on the farm by laying 3 inch clay pipes in a pattern of laterals, spaced 15 to 22 yards apart that connected to either 4 or 6 inch outfalls. I remember that Dowlmans haulage from Willoughby used to regularly deliver loads of "tiles" as they were commonly known, direct from The London Brick Companies works at Peterborough to the farm. The foot long cream, or sienna coloured pipes were rough to handle making for grazes and cuts on the inside of fingers, as the manufacturing and firing process left sharp edges within the tiles. The handling technique involved inserting fingers into two or three individual pipes and then to transfer them from the lorry to a carefully built tiered stack in the farm yard, or on some occasions in the field where they were going to be laid. Only the better quality, larger diameter pipes that were used for the main outfalls had a uniform smooth dark brown finish, whilst the exterior surface of the 3 inch pipes was either octagonal or given a corrugated profile as though they had been passed through a pastry mould.

The carpenters, Arthur and later Walt West played a very important part in village life for more than 70 years in their roles as undertakers. If someone died in the village, the West's suspended whatever job they were doing at that time, whilst they manufactured a coffin out of the large stock of coffin timbers that were stored in the workshop roof. The deceased body in those days was generally kept at home, for the few days, before burial in St. Leonard's Churchyard with the whole process from death to burial taking place comfortably inside a week.

Following Arthur's retirement Walt spent a large proportion of his time working for the farm, carrying out joinery reconstruction work either on houses or farm buildings. They carried out their business in a low, brick built, building with a painted, corrugated iron roof, whose outside wall fronted directly on to the road in Chapel Lane. Within their workshop they constructed almost every type of wooden structure that farms required, ranging from cattle feeding troughs, to gates and doors and even the construction of completely new buildings. Every year they manufactured quite a number of square tumbrels for local livestock farmers that were used for feeding hay and straw to cattle, housed in crew yards for the winter period. These flat bottomed, five foot square troughs standing about four feet tall were constructed of stout, four inch square, oak corner legs, and one inch boarded bottoms and sides, and were designed to hold squares of loose straw that the garthman carried by fork to the cattle. The Wests also constructed four wheeled, flat bed, farm trailers for bale leading, using second hand lorry axles for the running gear, and two circles of flat steel bar to form a turntable for the front steering axle.

Arthur West although quite small in stature was always immaculately dressed, as he generally wore a freshly laundered white apron every day. Walter West, although he was no relation, joined the business shortly before Arthur retired to live in the old vicarage, but there the similarity ended because although Arthur had quite a dour and serious countenance. Walter, was always laughing with a broad smile on his face that seemed to be accentuated by his mop of blonde hair.

I remember how Walt used to carefully remove a small well worn tin that contained his smokes, from an inside pocket and methodically extract a cigarette paper that he would adhere to his moistened upper lip, before filling it with tobacco, and in doing so would delight in relating a wealth of stories and anecdotes. A well practiced routine with lads who had recently left school and were assisting Walt when he was carrying out a repair job on the farm involved sending them on foolish errands that were designed to give everyone else a good laugh when they returned empty handed not realising until later how stupid they had been. As he removed a pinch of tobacco from the tin and meticulously rolled it into a stalk thin strip he would say, to a gullible youth who had either just left school or was working on the farm during school holidays.

"Tom can you just nip down to the shop and get me a packet of spirit level bubbles; I see that the one in my spirit levels got a hole in it, tell Mrs Griffen to put the cost onto Walt West's account".

The hapless young fellow eager to carry out an important errand would set off purposefully only to return despondently from the village shop with the news that, "Mrs Griffin, (who was well versed with these requests), says that she sold her last spirit level bubbles this morning".

However when he saw Walt and other workers exploding with laughter Tom quickly got the message that he wouldn't be falling for that sort of errand again.

This was but one of a number of hoary chestnuts that never seemed to lose their attraction, rather like a harmless initiation process they were trotted out regularly year after year to young people coming on to the farm for the first time. Many of the ruses involved sending a gullible youth to collect a "vital piece" of equipment from the back of an old building. If the young chap had just paused for thought and put his brain into gear he would surely have realised the stupidity of the request. A hardy standard was to collect a wool riddle, and if that request hadn't dented their confidence then an errand to the farm house to pick up a pint of pigeon milk might well have done, to say nothing of taking a delivery from Tetney treacle mines.

If a farm building or house needed repair then, of course, the Wests could deal with any type of work that used wood.

Walt West constructed the intricate wooden roof structures of our first home, "Te Anau", a dorma type house built in 1964. If the West's were not working with wood they were painting and decorating. At that time in the early sixties, the farm had, in addition to the farm houses several cottages for employees that provided a regular job of painting one house exterior each summer. During the winter, Walt carried out internal painting, wallpapering and any other alterations that were required. From my earliest recollections the carpenter or blacksmith could do any job on the farm or in the farmhouses except electrical or plumbing work.

CHAPTER 9
Beware the unexpected

I am reminded of a quotation by Benjamin Disraeli, when he stated that. "What we anticipate seldom occurs.

What we least expect generally occurs".

Of course his observation referred to his experience in politics, which is as true today as it was then, but he might equally well have had the unpredictability of cattle in mind.

Farming is regarded by the Health and Safety Executive as being by far the most hazardous industry, even surpassing that of fishing and construction.

Invariably the weather influences decisions that must be made quickly. Sometimes the unexpected occurs even after we have taken all reasonable precautions. Looking back over a lifetime spent working with livestock many of my scariest moments dealing with cattle have come from totally unexpected situations. Take the case of a particularly quiet cow that had given birth to a pair of twin calves one New Years eve.

The birth of twin calves invariably creates problems as sometimes both calves are presented at the same time resulting in a tangle of legs. Alternatively one of the calves is presented in a breach position, which means that the back legs are coming first.

Either situation requires some assistance on our part to ensure that both calves are delivered safely, but in this instance the cow had produced two healthy calves completely unaided.

In order that the calves would not wander away from their mother we decided to remove the three of them from the rest of the cows and calves in the crew yard, and put them into an adjoining stable.

Segregating freshly calved cows with their new born calves from the rest of the herd for the first couple of days, or until such time as we are confident that the calves are suckling unaided is routine procedure.

It's quite important that the calf receives its first drink of its mother's milk as soon as possible because it contains anti bodies in the colostrum, that are vital in raising resistance to many diseases.

The cow was a placid animal who had already gone through this procedure with her previous calves with no bother, so I had no reason to think that this was going to be anything other than a simple routine matter, even though she had a pair of twins on this occasion.

I fully expected that within the confined space of the stable that the active calves would soon discover their mother's udder and consequently would be little or no trouble.

It had been one of those gloomy cold days so typical of mid winter as Alistair (my 12 year old son) and I forked silage to the rest of the cattle that afternoon.

Before going for our tea, I carried a forkful of silage to the cow in the stable whilst Alistair, opened the wooden door allowing me to pass inside the brick building.

The stable had originally been built in Victorian times and was designed to hold a couple of horses, one on either side of a twenty foot wooden partition that divided the eighteen foot wide building into two equal halves.

Two brick arches standing approximately twenty inches above the ground formed the base of a stone feeding trough at the far end of the building, where the horses would originally have been fed cut oats.

A wooden slatted rack fastened to the brick wall was inclined at an angle above the stone trough and was designed to hold hay.

As I entered the building I noted that both of the calves were lying contentedly in the straw midway along the side of the wooden partition.

Not wishing to disturb them I carried the fork of silage past the cow to the feeding trough, noting by the size of her teats that the calves had been suckling.

The cow took a mouthful of silage, but before I had an opportunity to walk back to the stable door she spun round and in a flash butted her head at Alistair.

He had been standing just inside the closed stable door and was immediately flattened by the cow's headlong charge.

She snorted and bellowed as she buried her head into his chest, heaving his body against the brick wall.

Even though I was at the wrong end of the building I shouted and rushed to his rescue. The cow spun around once more and immediately set about me, but unfortunately I had no refuge as I was at the other end of the building.

As Alistair painfully scrambled to his feet, the cow remorselessly pummelled me with her head until she had managed to wedge me tightly under one of the two brick arches.

Alistair was naturally terrified, and to this day he can recall with vivid clarity the sequence of events that occurred that new year's eve more than twenty five years ago.

Having slammed the door shut he had the presence of mind to sufficiently distract the cow's attention from the safety of outside the stable door in order that I could extract myself from under the trough and make a lunge for the edge of the wooden hay rack.

Both of us suffered bruises and multiple grazing to our bodies.

Judging by the length of time it took for the pain in my chest to subside I feel sure that perhaps one or two ribs were cracked also. Fortunately neither of us had any other limbs broken when the outcome could well have been far more serious.

The general public are normally quite apprehensive when they see a full grown bull who may weigh anything up to a ton and a half, but from my experience cows with new born calves can be much more dangerous.

Every year there are reports of farmers and farm workers being killed or injured by normally quiet animals that for some unexpected reason act completely out of character.

Generally its one of the dairy breed of bulls that's responsible for the most serious accidents. Beef breeds tend to be much more docile.

Several accidents whereby members of the general public are attacked by cows defending their calves seem to occur every year.

In the great majority of cases they are caused by people walking with a dog in fields where cows and calves are grazing.

The cow sees the dog as a threat to their calf, as they are unable to distinguish the difference between a dog and their traditional enemy the wolf.

Sadly many of these incidents result in a fatality or at the very least someone being severely injured, as people make the error of rushing to the dogs defence, when in all reality the dog is generally more agile and more than capable of dodging the cow as it runs away.

Even a small dog with four legs can outrun a human being on two.

Even when the cows know us, the pain involved in giving birth can sometimes make the quietest of cows unpredictable as both Alistair and I discovered to our cost one summer.

Legislation following the B S E debacle in 1996 stipulated that all cattle should hold a passport that recorded their movements from farm to farm.

It required all calves to wear a unique ear tag that had to be applied within 28 days of birth in order that it matched the animal's passport details.

One summer's morning I discovered that a cow had calved rather unexpectedly in a remote field that we were renting for summer grazing. The calf had obviously suckled and was trotting quite happily by its mother's side, but we were presented with the problem of giving the calf its statutory ear tag.

If animals are not tagged DEFRA inspectors have the power to impose substantial fines on the farmer.

Unfortunately the field was more than three miles from the home farms and it would be another four months before we brought all the cattle back for the winter, so we thought that if we carefully planned the operation we could catch the calf in the field.

After all it would take less than a couple of minutes work to tag the calf, but we hadn't reckoned on the unexpected.

Two days later we decided to execute the plan.

It seemed reasonable to think that if I were to drive my Landrover slowly past the calf as it lay down that Alistair could open the back door of the vehicle and grab the calf before it realised what was happening.

The plan was that Adrian would slip out of the other door and hold the calf whilst Alistair popped the tags in the calf's ears.

It seemed perfect as the mother was grazing some distance away with the rest of the herd whilst the calf was laid in the lee of a large tussock of coarse grass.

I drove slowly by in such way that I didn't startle the calf.

Animals soon accept that a motor vehicle doesn't represent a threat to them, so will consequently allow you to drive quite close by them.

A situation that would be impossible on foot, as a young calf would be quite nervous if anyone approached too close to it.

As I drove by Alistair darted out the vehicle and before the calf knew what was happening he was laid over it, preventing it getting to its feet.

At that point before Adrian could get to him the calf let out the most terrified beal that had a dramatic effect to the rest of the herd including the calf's mother. They all ceased grazing and instantaneously lifted their heads and bealed back in response.

The mother though took to her heels and must have covered those fifty yards from where she was grazing at what seemed like the speed of light, so that before Alistair had an opportunity to release the calf she was on to him, burrowing her head into his body. She continued to roll him over whilst buffeting him with her head.

The other two of us immediately went to his assistance and received equal treatment as she attacked us in turn before we all feeling rather bruised managed to get behind the Landrover.

I seem to recall that we left the calf untagged for the remainder of the summer and only tagged it when it returned to the home farm with the rest of the herd in the autumn. If the inspector had called in the meantime and insisted that the calf be tagged immediately he may have heard a few choice words.

Following a severe gale that blew all one Friday we discovered late that afternoon that the wind had demolished one of the five foot clear plastic sheets from the roof above one of our grain stores.

Heavy rain was forecast for later that evening so mindful of the damage that rain pouring off the roof would inflict on the grain we had little option other than to replace the broken sheet before darkness fell.

Well aware of the dangers of working on roofs Alistair and I were safely ensconced within the safety platform attached to the front of our JCB telescopic fork lift, as Adrian lifted us up to roof level at the gable end of the building.

In addition to the various tools that we needed to carry out the job we took a number of crawling boards in order that our weight would be more evenly distributed over the corrugated roof.

The roof pitches on modern clear span agricultural buildings is at a much shallower pitch than on domestic houses, so that repair work can be carried out more easily provided that weight is evenly spread over the brittle fibre roofing sheets.

Our 12 foot crawling boards led us some distance from the gable end, across the roof to where the hole was, so that we were then able to surround the hole with boards and set about the task of replacing the broken sheet with a new one.

First though we had to unwind the screw nails that secured the adjoining roof sheets on to the underlying wooden purling so that we could slide the replacement sheet underneath.

Once a pair of mole grips was fastened on to the small domed nail head it meant exerting considerable leverage with our arms to unwind the nail, which in turn caused the crawling board on which we were crouching to shift slightly as we exerted more pressure.

It was at that point that if we had been apprehensive of the task confronting us before, then we certainly were then.

It was still blowing a stiff wind that seemed to be much stronger on the exposed roof than it was down at ground level.

Was it the fear of the unexpected that made it feel even colder as the wind tugged at our clothing?

However it was imperative that we complete the task as quickly as possible as the light was already beginning to fade.

All of a sudden we heard a rumbling noise and spotted our tool box sliding slowly down the roof.

Over the years a thin film of yellow coloured lichen had colonised the roof, and it was over this surface that the metal toolbox was sliding at a steady speed.

"Don't try and rescue it", Alistair shouted as the toolbox containing battery powered equipment reached the edge of the building before disappearing over the side.

Then one of the crawling boards that we weren't standing on started to move, and that really alarmed us.

Almost like the final scene of "The Italian Job", where the rear of the gang's bus is balancing over the edge of a vast drop to the valley hundreds of feet below, we hesitated as we decided what we should do next.

The gale had dried the surface of the lichen although it was damp underneath, and this had created ideal conditions for the wind to push the metal toolbox and allow it to start sliding.

We realised that it only required a small amount of pressure on the crawling boards and they would follow a similar path to the toolbox.

By distributing our weight over more boards we kept any other sliding to a minimum so that after half an hour's anxious work we successfully completed the task.

Over confidence coupled with the inexperience of youth frequently leads to unexpected events occurring as I vividly remember from my early days on the farm.

I had only been working on the farm for a year or so when a neglected hedge was reduced in height in order that it could be trimmed with a hedge knife.

As this was some time before the first mechanical hedge cutters appeared, it was essential that hedges were kept reasonably compact; otherwise it was impossible to trim them with the traditional hand held hedge knife.

The hedge knife was commonly known as a slasher because there was quite an art in the way that the hedger flicked his wrist so that the ten inch single blade would cleanly cut springy twigs.

It's quite possible that the hedge hadn't been trimmed for more than thirty years; consequently it had grown to a considerable height resulting in a large volume of woody material being removed and laid alongside the hedge in preparation for it being burnt.

A few years earlier the farm had purchased one of the first tractor mounted fore end loaders to come on to the market which was attached to one of our petrol paraffin grey Ferguson tractors.

It was called a Horndraulic loader that utilised Harry Fergusons revolutionary hydraulic system to power the lifting arms.

Seen from today's perspective it was quite a lethal bit of machinery, bearing in mind that the tractor on which it was mounted was completely open as it lacked the safety of a modern tractor cab.

However in those days this was a revolutionary bit of kit because its tines could lift perhaps a quarter of a ton of manure at a time when previously the job had all been done by hand.

Unfortunately the positioning of the hydraulic rams and stay bars on either side of the tractor produced a scissor like action as the hydraulic rams were extended or contracted.

Should the tractor driver lean sideways over the mudguards as the loader was being lowered there was every chance that he would be decapitated. Never the less the device soon found lots of other uses apart from loading manure.

By running the loader bucket along the ground it was able to push the great piles of briars and thorn branches removed from the hedge on to heaps where it could be burned.

It was quite difficult to get the green wood to start burning, but once a good core of hot embers was established it was simply a matter of taking the tractor and loader to the field on a daily basis to push more material on to the fire.

I had watched one of the farm workers carry out the task on previous days and saw how he pushed a great pile of wood and thorny material right on to the very fire itself.

I noted how he drove the tractor right up to the fire, then amidst a hail of sparks as the briars within the material burst into flame he quickly selected reverse gear and backed away.

I volunteered to carry out the operation the following day as I was used by then to driving a tractor, though I really had done little work using the fore end loader.

All went well as I collected a great heap of thorns and pushed them along the ground to the fire.

I saw how the lighter material burst into flame as I depressed the clutch pedal and sharply pulled the gear lever out of second gear in order that I could select reverse gear.

Then panic!

I probably hadn't fully depressed the clutch, and in my haste to select reverse gear I must have snatched the gear lever back too sharply, because the lever came out of its selector so that it was impossible for me to select reverse gear.

By now the heat was intense on my face and to compound my fear one of the front tyres was starting to smoke.

One of the problems with those early fore end loaders lay in the fact that the gear selectors became worn after a season's work of cleaning out the manure in a crewyard. After all it involved many thousands of repetitive gear changes and if the clutch pedal wasn't fully depressed on every occasion wear took place.

I had seen how this had happened once before in the farm yard and watched how the driver had removed the two nuts that held the gear stick in place.

He had then slipped the end of the gear lever into the selector that was still engaged, after which he was able to get the gear that he wanted.

I had been warned not to snatch at the gears because this might happen, so what was I going to say when I had to report that I had managed to incinerate one of the farms tractors.

I don't think I considered that immediately in front of me was a tank of highly inflammable fuel, as I reached my hand into the toolbox and removed the Fergie spanner whose small end would fit the two nuts.

In spite of the heat I managed to unscrew the nuts and retract the selector.

As I reversed away from the fire the rubber on one of the tyres started to burn, but I was clear thank goodness.

CHAPTER 10
End of an Era

Watching a cream and blue Greyscroft bus negotiate the sharp bend that was always known as Humberston's corner, on its journey from Louth to Mablethorpe, I am reminded of the selfless couple that devoted much of their lives to the upkeep of the village church. Arthur Humberston and his wife Margaret lived in a mud and stud cottage situated tight on the corner a wooden gate let into a immaculately trimmed, privet hedge opened onto a narrow brick path that in spring was generally bordered by sweet smelling Brompton Stocks and wallflowers. Later in the year they would be replaced by a sea of multi- coloured Sweet Williams. Sunlight glinted off the roof that must once have been thatched but was now covered with red painted, corrugated iron roofing sheets. Two small windows were let into the wall on either side of the west facing door that led into the small house. During the summer months the walls on either side of the windows were cloaked with red roses flowering in profusion against the uneven surface of the white, lime-washed walls.

Beyond the house lay the vegetable garden, fully stocked with a wide selection of vegetables growing in soil that always seemed to be completely devoid of weeds. Further up the garden they grew raspberries, strawberries and other soft fruit protected from birds under a well constructed netted cage. The Humberstons were entirely sufficient in fruit and vegetables, as Margaret carefully bottled surplus summer fruits for winter consumption. Through their skilful endeavours Margaret was able to provide a regular supply of flowers for the Altar at St Leonard's church from their garden.

Margaret's erect figure and sharp facial features with immaculately coiffured hair, neatly tied into a bun, contrasted sharply with Arthurs stooped figure, who like so many men at that time had probably acquired a bent back as a result of a lifetime's manual work. Margaret generally wore long, floral print dresses, and spoke in a very quiet precise manner giving the impression that she was the dominant partner in the marriage. Arthur by contrast was a rather humble, mild mannered man quite content with his lot holding no aspirations to own more worldly goods than were strictly necessary. The little house, though simply furnished, was kept immaculately clean and tidy by Margaret. Fresh flowers gave brightness and colour to the darkest recesses of the poorly lit rooms on even the darkest of winter days. Arthur was one of the last of a breed of smallholders, who managed to earn a living from a paddock at the rear of his house, along with two other equally small paddocks in the village, that combined would total little more than 5 acres. He kept a couple of milking cows, along with a sow and a few sheep and poultry.

He was listed in Kelly's 1930 Directory of Lincolnshire as being a cottage farmer: a class of people that would be obsolete less than 25 years later. Particularly on a still summers evening they could both be seen cycling seperately around the village on their two ancient sit up and beg cycles which represented their sole means of private transport. Margaret generally cycled a little ahead of her husband. Her slim figure dressed in a long coat that draped decorously on either side of the screened back wheel of her cycle.

Arthur conveyed hay and straw that he needed for his animals on a wooden flat bedded cart, which he pushed or pulled by means of two waist high handles. He kept his few livestock in a variety of neat wooden buildings in the paddock that was reached by means of a narrow track leading off the road alongside the rear of the house. From time to time we would hear the rhythmic drumming of metal rimmed wheels passing over the lane's stoned surface, heralding Arthur's approach to our farmyard. On arrival he would disentangle himself from within the two wooden handles, then as he straightened his knees he would push out his chest in order to reach a semi vertical position and make his familiar pronouncement, which of course from past experience we knew exactly what he meant. *"Hev yer got eny kozy toshers?"*. What he called "kozy toshers" was in fact a brand of cooked, flaked maize known as Kositos. He used this to supplement the cereal diet for his livestock, but as the suppliers only delivered in ton lots he would purchase the odd couple of bags from us which would last him for several weeks.

Both of them were great stalwarts of St Leonard's church in South Cockerington. Margaret cleaned and cared for the inside of the building, whilst Arthur as church sexton cared for the fabric of the church he also maintained the church yard and trimmed the yew hedge. He dug graves and scythed the churchyard grass that once dry he would load on to his handcart and pull home to be used for his cattle's winter feed.

As I survey the scene set out before me from this ageless vantage point of Conscience Hill, I ponder on the reason why there is no human habitation within at least 400 yards of this commanding lookout, especially as churches tended to be built on the highest ground in a village. Wherever I look over the marsh, I can see numerous church towers in addition to the tall spires at Louth and South Somercotes whose structures were designed to reach up as far as possible towards the heavens, so I wonder why this high spot has not been settled and even more why a church was never built here. Could it be that the conscience Hill rock that I refer to on the first page was not left by the ice age but was in fact taken there by human hand to be used in some form of pagan worship.

Religion has always played a fundamental part in the development of villages such as South Cockerington with the close interaction of church and state that is so graphically illustrated by the history of the Scrope family, and the Vavasours before them. When Ralph Scrope first gazed over his freshly acquired lands, from Conscience Hill he would have easily spotted the tower of the green sandstone church tower, that stood within a few yards of his home at the Manor House. As he swivelled round and looked due west I'm sure that he could have hardly failed but be impressed by the massive walls of the Abbey and the destruction that had so recently taken place. Raising his eyes, he would have seen the towering 300 feet, tall spire of St James church a couple of miles beyond which made it one of the tallest buildings in Britain at the time. The nave and chancel of St Leonard's church was built of Spilsby green sandstone and Ancaster stone, very similar materials to those used for the construction of the nearby Louth Abbey. It's fairly certain that the Vavasour family commissioned the construction of the church as they were the principle landowners of the estate for over 200 years, before the arrival of Ralph Scrope. However the tower is the oldest part of the building, constructed of limestone and green sandstone and predates the chancel and nave which has Tudor designed windows, so the present church could well have been on the site of a much earlier building. One of the three bells is dated 1286 and the other two 1726. The churches most notable feature is its magnificently carved, 15th century Rood screen that thanks to the endeavours of the Rev James Smart who was vicar from 1931 - 1953 was restored during the darkest days of the last war in 1940. For reasons unknown the screen was dismantled, possibly during major restoration work that was carried out in 1873 when half of it was sold for a sovereign!

During the early years of the 19th century there was a desire by many working people to break away from the authoritarian domination of the Anglican Church. This was led by the Wesleys crusades to establish Methodism. The successes of the movement in Louth influenced the desire for people in the villages to have their own local chapel consequently in 1837 a Wesleyan Methodist Chapel was built on the site of today's "Tudor Lodge" in Chapel Lane South Cockerington. However the Methodists broke away into various factions with the Free Methodists wishing to follow a path with political allegiance to the Liberal party, leading them to construct a massive Corinthian columned 1200 seat chapel in Louth's, Eastgate.. Wishing to follow suit the Free Methodists purchased a 42x31 feet plot of land 50 yards beyond the Wesleyan Chapel in 1855 for £25.

Obviously the small village populationof those days could neither warrant nor sustain three places of worship, so in 1902 the two chapels amalgamated in the Free Methodists building with the word "free" covered over. Until the late 1950's the chapel was still the centre of many people's lives. Many Methodists attending two services every Sunday and widespread support for a thriving Sunday school. Although our family were members of St Leonard's congregation, with my father a long standing church warden, we nevertheless attended the chapel harvest festival and auction of garden produce in October, and the Anniversary in May when the Sunday school children recited poetry or sang.

Towards the end of June the vicarage garden was bedecked with bunting ready for the annual garden fete, which, in addition to being an enjoyable social event, created funds for the upkeep of the village Church. The fete was an eagerly anticipated event drawing visitors from many of the surrounding villages allowing people, devoid of rival attractions, to dress up and meet folk they had not met for sometime when they could chat over sandwiches and cakes, and drink tea in the vicarage conservatory. They could bowl for a pig, or blast heavy wooden balls at wooden skittles, or if they were less energetic see how good an aim they had at a dart board. There were guessing competitions, and if that didn't suit they could always purchase armfuls of wholesome fresh produce. Sadly by the 70s the established order was rapidly changing due to many factors. The rapid contraction of village tradesmen and vastly reduced numbers of people earning a living from agriculture, resulted in traditional village families moving away. The chapel closed in 1970, and the church authority's continued to amalgamate even more parishes under the responsibility of one vicar. Along with North Cockerington and Alvingham, South Cockerington's vicar was combined with Grimoldby and Manby under the care of Canon Hanson living at Grimoldby vicarage.

Nostalgic memories of the Humberstons and village life in the 1950s lead me to remember other village occupations that have now passed into history. Sixty years ago farming support was supplied by village based craftsman such as Fred Phillipson the blacksmith who could do almost as much with metal as his carpenter counterparts the West's could do with anything constructed of wood.

Today our sophisticated farm machinery requires specialist knowledge from teams of well trained technicians such as those from Peacock and Binnington, the local Massey Ferguson dealer in Louth who supply much of our machinery. They give us excellent service, particularly at

Fergie tractor towing a combination grain and fertilizer drill in the southern half of Mill Hill. Circa 1956. Note the sea defence piping that formed the fence dividing the arable part of the field from the grass part. Photo courtesy of Mrs M Bathurst.

the critical harvest period with twenty four hour back up for the range of tractors, combine, fork lift and other machinery they have supplied to us. From my very earliest recollections, dating back to the mid 1940s I vividly remember Fred Phillipson, the blacksmith from Alvingham, who manned a satellite blacksmith shop in the village one day a week. The rhythmical, bell like, sound of his hammer striking metal echoed around the village, as he pounded red hot horse shoes into shape over the massive anvil. Fred was of medium height, though slightly stooped as befitted a man who had spent a lifetime hauling up the feet of immense Shire horses, in order that he could shoe them. His heavily muscled arms and shoulders rippled, like the ebb tide on a sandy beach, as a consequence of spending a lifetime wielding iron against iron. A broad, leather belt supported a pair of well worn trousers whilst his blackened flat cap was always worn at an angle. My first vision of Fred was of a figure bent almost double as he straddled over the raised back leg of a seemingly giant horse with his back in the firing line for anything that may drop from under the animal's tail.

As I got closer, more of his figure materialized from within a pulsating cloud of white smoke and my nostrils picked up the acrid smell of burning hoof. Fred gripping the mass of hair above one hoof with one hand, raised an enormous foot and then, with a deftness gained by many years of experience, clasped a red hot, iron horse shoe on to the sole of the horse's hoof with a pair of tongs. The throat gagging smoke swirled from between the tiles of the low roofed building, drowning the smoke from the cigarette that Fred habitually had in the corner of his mouth. The pan tiled brick building in South View Lane was overshadowed by several large, cherry plum trees that during the dank days of winter contributed to the buildings internal gloom. The walls of the smoky interior were lined with a vast selection of different sized rusty horseshoes festooned in a complex network of dusty cobwebs. In one corner of the small work shop stood a six foot square, by four foot high, brick forge containing a dull red fire of glowing coals. This could quickly be aroused to fearsome intensity by an ancient pensioner who sat hunched up beside the forge, when on Fred's command he could be galvanised into action rhythmically pumping a long handled wooden shaft that operated the leather bellows. Fred didn't have welding equipment at that time; so consequently, any metal repairs had to either be riveted or forged together, by heating both pieces of iron until they were white hot in the forge, then hammering them both together on the anvil. Large water tanks constructed of riveted, sheet metal plate were required on livestock farms as they were a vital necessity to store rainwater for the cattle to drink over the winter months. Unfortunately from time to time these tanks developed leaks and consequently Fred had to carry out repairs patching the hole with a riveted metal plate.

Water from the overhead tank at Ram Corner (As mentioned earlier) was used to fill a large metal tank mounted on an iron wheeled metal chassis for supplying water to various groups of livestock either in the fields or outlying cattle yards.

Because the trailer wasn't sprung the tank vibrated and bounced as it travelled over road or field, resulting in the metal tank constantly chafing against other parts of the metal chassis. It eventually wore holes in the metal plate and required fairly regular attention to repair leaks to the bottom of the tank. Because of my smaller size as a child, I remember having to crawl inside the narrow opening at the top of the tank, now lying on its side, to push white hot rivets through drilled holes and then hold a heavy hammer against the rivet whilst Fred riveted it from the outside. With the absence of ear defenders you can imagine how it sounded to me crouched within that metal tank!.

Can you imagine a child being allowed to do that today?

In addition to carrying out repairs and manufacturing gate crooks and the like, the two main stays of his business were shoeing horses and repairing harrows. When harrow tines wore down and lost their pointed ends he removed each tine in turn, then after heating it, alongside another piece of metal in the forge, to a white hot state, combined both pieces of metal together by hammering them on the anvil to form either a pointed end or a curved foot known as a duck foot harrow. Fred's skill was always in demand and especially so at harvest time, when he was constantly on call to adjust the notoriously temperamental tying mechanism on binders. Frustratingly, at times the binder refused to tie a knot around a sheaf of corn, resulting in a succession of loose bundles of grain stalks. Noting the plea of urgency, Fred, who was a man of few words would leave whatever job he was doing at the time and drive straight to the field in his old pre-war Ford car, where his deliberate actions and confident air of authority quickly diffused many a stressful situation. Clutching a leather handled, hessian bag that contained a suitable collection of hammers and a variety of spanners, Fred would set off purposely with his head bent low walking at a brisk pace across the rows of spiky stubble to the broken down binder. Fred was a jovial man with big, black ingrained hands, but probably as a consequence of a lifetime's hammering metal on an anvil, was rather hard of hearing. I always remember him as being very positive, when his answer to any problem would be, *"Yiss, we can do it"*.

In the early fifties he closed the Cockerington satellite workshop; in order that he could concentrate his work at the Alvingham forge. The building which we owned was cleared of ironwork and then for a number of years served as a calf creep for young bulls by leaving a restricted entrance in the doorway that allowed calves to enter and eat concentrates, but because of the limited size of the opening the mothers were excluded By the early seventies the roof rotted and it was demolished, leaving the foundations which are still visible, to this day, in the grounds of a new bun galow.

CHAPTER 11
An Agricultural Revolution

From where I sit on this glorious evening, I can see tractors working in all directions as everyone takes advantage of the settled spell of weather allowing them to plough and cultivate, and in our case crack on with cultivations in order that we can endeavour to complete all our autumn sowing by early October.

August and September are now one of the busiest periods in the early twenty first century farming calendar, as the majority of farms in this area have now specialised in arable farming. This is in sharp contrast to the position fifty years ago when most farmers in the district would have had some form of livestock enterprise, in addition to their arable land resulting in a high proportion of their crops being planted 'in the Spring. At that time, in spite of ploughing seed land, (a temporary one year grass/clover break crop), in late July in preparation for winter wheat, no one would contemplate drilling until early October for fear of the crop becoming too 'winter proud'. In any event, harvesting would generally continue until mid September, followed by many days of collecting and stacking bales. During the early 60's to mid 70s it became common practice to tow a bale sledge behind a baler with a man stacking the bales up to seven high on the sledge, before pushing the pack backwards over a series of wooden rollers onto the receding ground as the baler and sledge moved forward.

Leading bales, in the 50s and 60s was extremely hard back breaking work, resulting in straw scratched hands and arms, and very sore fingers from lifting the bales by their strings. Bale leading commenced on the completion of combining and took seven or eight of us almost two weeks to complete the task. We filled all the Dutch barns adjacent to the various cattle yards, in addition to building other stacks nearby. Two men called "pickers "stuck their forks into the top of a bale, and then with a synchronised action heaved the bale over their heads on to a trailer. This operation was superseded, a few years later, when a bale lifter attached to a front end loader was invented. By operating a hydraulic ram the attachment gripped a stack of six or eight bales and lifted them on to a trailer.

Lewis Parkinson (with his daughter Dorothy),   at the controls of our first self propelled combine harvester, A Massey Harris 726 late 1940s. Photo courtesy of Mrs M Bathurst.

Grimoldby Grange creamery 1950s Photo courtesy of Mrs D Partridge, nee Marriott.

112

Three tractor drivers stacked their own load of bales in the field, then drove to the yard where they emptied their trailers on to an elevator which conveyed them either into a Dutch barn or onto a stack.

Two men passed the bales across the stack to the stacker, who carefully bound the courses so that the stack did not collapse as it got higher. Our farm would have been typical of many marsh farms during the 1950s and 60s. When more than half a farms total acreage was either under permanent grass or in short term grass and clover leys. These forage break crops were rotated around the arable fields and were either grazed with livestock or mowed, for hay when the dried baled material was known as "seeds".

Grass and clover was generally sown within a growing crop of either spring oats or barley, known as 'under sowing', with the intention of getting the crop established for use the following year after the current crop had been harvested. Ryegrass, and particularly Red Clover could sometimes grow too well in a wet summer, with the result that the cereal crop was often swamped with lush vegetation. This made harvesting extremely difficult, as the crop was then so full of green material that the straw could never dry properly, resulting in not only high losses of grain being carried over the back of the combine with the damp straw, but also a poor grain sample due to the inclusion of bits of green grass and clover.

Our large herd of Lincoln Red Cattle were grazed on a combination of temporary grass leys and permanent grass fields during the summer months, after which they were wintered in large, partially open, crew yards and fed on the arable by-products of wheat, barley and oat straw, supplemented by the 'seeds hay' (the red clover, rye grass mixture).

Years of breeding and selection had led to the Lincoln Red breed being developed to lay down fat during the summer and then live economically on a low nutritional, arable by-products diet during the winter.

In 1945 there were twenty two farms and small holdings in the village provided a living for the owner and his family, in addition to providing a living for at least another twenty two other additional workers and their families. Every farm carried one or more kinds of large livestock with at least eight of them having milking herds, easily identified by the silver metalled 10 gallon churns standing on a wooden platform outside the farm gate awaiting collection by lorry for the Co-Op creamery at Grimoldby Grange. (See the separate chapter on Grimoldby Grange and the creamery.)

Today there are only two farming businesses left who reside in the village and only one farm worker. In addition, ours is the the last remaining farm to breed livestock with our herd of pedigree Charolais cattle. Such is the speed of change that over the last 40 years the sight of cattle grazing fields has almost vanished. Fifty years ago the very name of Charolais would have produced a similar blank expression on the face of local farmers as if they had been asked what Alpha Centauri was. (It's the nearest star apart from our sun to earth).

As I sit in on a comfortable tractor seat looking down the hill in an easterly direction, I remember the years before Conscience Hill was under drained and all three parts amalgamated. I vividly recall my time spent feeding lambing ewes, in the twenty six acres below me. In late February the heavily pregnant ewes were fed a supplementary diet of meal in wooden troughs to provide extra nourishment for the growing lambs that they were carrying. The journey up to the field by Landrover entailed a hazardous drive, negotiating a heavily rutted, muddy track alongside a branch of Monks Dyke, from the farm to the bottom part of Conscience Hill. It was extremely difficult task to stand upright whilst I carried a bag of meal across a seething morass of Wellington boot sucking, mud, created by hundreds of sheep's feet churning the ground into the consistency of sticky toffee. As I poured the contents of the bag into a line of wooden troughs the position became even more perilous as the ewes pushed and jostled, desperate to grab an extra mouthful of the sweet tasting meal.

During my early farming years, in the 1950s, the majority of jobs on farms were not only very hard work, but were also very labour intensive as so much work was still done by hand. However as a direct consequence of the 1947 Agriculture Act and the introduction of generous capital grants, money was made available to enable farmers to restructure their farms, by making massive investments in buildings and drainage, with the result that machines started to replace some of the hard, physical labour. The deficiency payment scheme introduced by the same act worked incredibly well for British agriculture by giving farmers a guaranteed base price for the commodities that they were producing. The result was that the U.K was largely self-sufficient in temperate food products, and by doing so, created cheap food, in order that the UKs manufactured goods could be competitively priced in overseas markets.

Harry Ferguson's brilliant invention just after the second world war, of incorporating hydraulics within the body of his distinctive grey 'Fergie tractors was arguably the greatest single invention in all of agricultural history. It introduced a startling new concept, that over the following years completely revolutionised agricultural work. For the very first time it provided mechanical power to lift and move bulky agricultural products that hither too had relied on human muscle power involving a great deal of hard, manual labour.

Prior to the widespread use of combine harvesters in the 1950s crops of grain were handled on at least seventeen separate occasions, from binding the crop in the field until the eventual farmyard manure was returned back to the land. My first job on the farm, as a 10 year old, was to lead a pair of shire horses pulling a trailer from stowk to stowk in the harvest field, whilst two men pitched sheaves, and a third loaded the sheaves on to the trailer. After the binding machine had cut the corn and made the sheaves they were gathered together in rows of 8 or 10 sheaves to form tent like

Binding Spring Barley 1951 at Grimoldby Grange. Photo courtesy Mrs D Partridge.

structures with their heads uppermost to dry. Generally three trailers led the sheaves to the stack yard so once a trailer had been loaded it would be unhitched for a tractor to tow it back to the yard where another gang would stack the sheaves.

Corn stacks were built in rows leaving sufficient room between the stacks to accommodate the threshing machine that threshed the sheaves of corn during the winter months. The construction of the stack commenced from a relatively small base called the steadle, with sheaves being placed stalk ends to the outside of the stack and heads pointing to the inside. It was built in such a way that kept the middle of the stack slightly higher than the outside edge. Each succeeding layer was placed slightly further out than the one below it, enabling the stack to form the traditional oval shape as it bulged outwards giving it a characteristically domed top to stop wet penetrating the stacks interior.

During the winter months a threshing machine was pulled alongside each stack. Then a straw elevator butted up to the end of the machine where the threshed straw emerged. A long flat belt, crossed to reverse the drive, provided the power as it led from a tractor pulley to the threshing

Lorry discharging grain onto a ship at Grimsby docks 1964, Note the sacks of grain and the way that they were loaded onto the lorry.

machine with another flat belt or alternatively an auxiliary Petter engine to take the drive to the straw elevator. The elevator was a long trough about fifty feet long by four feet wide pivoted at the intake end, and raised by two wire ropes suspended on two vertical poles approximately eighteen feet high and positioned halfway along the trough. A series of large metal tines bolted to chain driven lateral bars conveyed the loose straw up the trough to the centre of the stack so that the three stackers could fork the straw as they built the stack higher. Theirs was an extremely tiring job as they had to work in waist deep straw, forking a product that was light and fluffy. Their feeling of tiredness was accentuated by the hypnotic sound of the threshing drum murmuring away in the distance accompanied by the rhythmically clanking of the elevator chains passing over the elevators various sprockets and idlers. Fine chaff came out the bottom of the threshing machine whilst the pulse, which consisted mainly of leafy bits of straw, came out the back of the machine just below the straw walkers. Chaffing was a dirty, arduous job, usually given to two youths at the bottom rung of the farming ladder. It involved raking the chaff onto a seven feet square sheet of canvas. Then by means of pulling together cords attached to the four corners they would carry the filled sheet up an inclined broad plank to the very roof of the chaff house in order that the building could be completely filled to the rafters.

The small glaums of chaff, shaped rather like ladybird wings, surrounding the grains of wheat, were highly valued and kept separate from the other chaff, as it was mixed with meal during the winter months to bulk up the concentrates fed to cattle. Barley chaff was particularly nasty to deal with, as the barbed horns found their way into clothing and down the chaffers neck. In spite of wearing goggles it got into eyes and ears where it combined with the clouds of dust that constantly encircled them whilst working under the threshing machine.

Three men forked sheaves on the corn stack with the last man placing the sheaves within hands reach of the man who was feeding the threshing drum. There was quite a hierarchy in threshing machine work as the best job generally went to the man standing on the top of the machine. He cut the binder twine securing the sheaves and then fed the stalks of grain into the open rasp bars of the rapidly revolving threshing drum. Next in order of rank, was the corn man who stood alongside the drive belt at the opposite end of the machine to where the straw emerged. His duty was to weigh off the graded grain passing through a rotary screen and delivered a series of outlets into large, jute bags, hired from a sack contractors such as the railway company or Foxes, (Foxes was short for Chisholm, Fox and Garner).

As all grain was transported in hired sacks, there was a nationwide distribution service, with hiring centres based at the larger grain merchants and railway goods yards. Because rats destroyed so many sacks, there was a constant job, on wet days, to repair them by sowing on patches, or shortly before sacks became redundant, glueing on a patch with copydex.

For many years whilst still a small boy I could never understand why a large metal advertising sign attached to the gable end of a house at Gayton Top between Great Carlton and Withern should be prominently displaying in large letters,

"HIRE FOXES".

I knew that Foxes were notorious killers and regarded as a major pest causing havoc in a chicken house if the slide had not been properly closed, which naturally induced frenetic activity and a rush for a gun whenever a fox was spotted. To my young mind I could not understand why, in view of the devastation that these animals caused, anybody in their right mind would want to hire them. It was only much later that I learned that the advert was for a company by the name of Fox who hired sacks for storing grain!

Corn was weighed by the volume of grain taken to fill a standard sized sack, comprising 12 stone for oats, 16 stones for barley, 18 stones for wheat and 19 stones for peas and beans.

Sacks of grain were weighed on a platform weighing machine, and then conveyed by a two wheeled running barrow onto the platform of what was termed a winding barrow, that rather resembled a much larger version of a running barrow. By means of turning a large handle on the side of the winding barrow a chain that was connected to the platform holding the sack of grain, was wound around a shaft that lifted the platform up to shoulder height. Gripping the tied neck of the sack the corn man laid the sack across his shoulder and carried it up a flight of steps to the granary.

A good days threshing would produce about 18-20 tonnes of wheat consisting of approximately 180 – 200, 18 stone sacks.

By way of contrast our Massey Ferguson combine discharging grain on the move, comfortably harvests the 62 acres of Mill Hill in one working day. It yielded 285 tonnes in 2008, the equivalent of 2659 - 18 stone bags whilst employing just three people to carry out the entire operation.

This graphically illustrates how mechanisation has revolutionised harvesting over the last half century.

The combine harvester, with its three hundred and sixty horse-power engine and its twenty five foot cutting width, utilising on board computers linked to G.P.S. will produce yield maps showing the variability of output throughout the field. The combine has a consistent output of almost 40 tons per hour and will harvest as much grain in half an hour as it would have taken ten men a full day using a threshing machine 60 years ago.

The grain from this combine's seven and a half ton, onboard tank, can be automatically emptied on the move into a grain trailer travelling alongside that conveys the grain to various grain stores on the farm, one of which is a thousand ton round silo that can be filled by an auger at the rate of two tons every minute.

After a few weeks the straw in the straw stack settled and in the process lost about a third of its original height, making it much easier to cut with a cutting knife. Depending on the type of straw, it would either be used for feeding, or bedding by garthmen, whose sole employment over the winter period was to care for the cattle at their respective yards. The garthmen cut the straw stack into a series of roughly, four foot square slices, rather like cutting small cubes of bread from the side of a loaf. A 2ft 6 inch long, by 6 inch wide sharply pointed knife was thrust into the straw by means of a wooden handle fixed at right angles to the blade. In order for the knife to penetrate the straw it had to be exceptionally sharp so it constantly required sharpening by use of a carborundum rub stone, shaped rather like a grey cucumber that bulged in the middle.

The cut square of straw was then picked up by inserting a two pronged garthing fork into the centre of the square, and, by dexterous foot work the square of straw was transferred onto the garthman's back as he stepped sideways onto a wooden stabbared ladder propped up on the stack side, adjacent to the cut square. With the weight of the straw transferred via the fork on to his back he would carry it into the crew yard for either bedding or place it into a wooden tumbrel for feed.

At Hill House farm, chaff was stored in a steeply pitched, pan tile roofed barn. However, due to its deteriorating condition, the roof was removed in 1979 and replaced with a sledge roof laid over telegraph poles. The fine wheat chaff was stored at one end of the building, whilst the longer leaves known as pulse, from wheat and oat straw were stored at the other end.

There was a similar arrangement at Hall Farm, where in addition to the chaff house, there was a granary, now used as a cattle building. It had a wooden floor raised about four feet above the bare earth. Iron grills let into the brickwork provided ventilation. Sacks of grain were stored two high in here with generally one or two riders laid at right angles across the top of the sacks, but because of the earthen floor rats abounded resulting in serious damage to the sacks if they were stored for any length of time.

In the spring after the cattle had gone out to grass, accumulated manure in the cattle crew yards could be as much as three feet deep. Until the introduction of the first tractor mounted fore end loaders, utilising Harry Fergusons hydraulic system, it had to be forked by hand onto trailers, and transported to the one year clover/rye grass leys where it was heaped into enormous 'muck hills'. Two months later, the now rotted manure, was forked back onto trailers, and spread by hand on the land before being ploughed in.

By way of contrast loading manure from the crew yards today is a very easy operation. Our JCB fork lift pushes a 6 feet wide manure bucket, with eight three inch wide hardened steel tines, into the solid manure. Hydraulic rams exert downward pressure onto the encompassing grab, enabling other rams to crowd back exerting many tons of tear out pressure, before lifting three tons of manure at a time and depositing it into a eighteen ton trailer. By using a fork lift and grab, one man can load as much manure on to a trailer in five minutes as it would have taken three men working exceptionally hard more than half a day in the 1940s.

Our 'round' baler produces big bales of straw, hay and silage, with some silage bales weighing almost a ton each. Bales are picked up two at a time by the grab on the JCB fork lift that places seventeen of them on a flat bed trailer for transport to the farmyard. With great dexterity they are lifted off the trailer and stacked, two at a time, up to six bales high, giving an overall height of more than 24 feet. Today cattle are fed and bedded using the same fork lift, to either deposit bales of silage directly into large round feeders, or spread bales of straw from the jaws of the hydraulic grab.

Our JCB forklift carrying two big straw bales of straw equal to about 25 small bales.

If I had been armed with a pair of binoculars during the winter sixty years ago, my panoramic view would have enabled me to observe lots of men 'hedging' throughout the middle marsh area. Many of them would have worn hob-nailed boots and ex army canvas leggings, and been similarly dressed to keep warm in a khaki, ex-army, great coat purchased from Clark,s ex WD (War Department) clothing section at the rear of their hardware shop in Louth's Queen Street. Head gear generally consisted of a flat cap. Hedging entailed using a knife, known as a 'slasher', which had a very sharp, ten inch long by three inches wide blade attached to a five foot long, wooden shaft. A swift upward movement cut the springy hawthorn twigs, which were then collected, along with the scythed grass fronting the hedge called the 'brea', into heaps which were generally burnt on the site.

Ditching men often followed the hedgers in situations where a ditch ran alongside a hedge. Once the hedge had been trimmed, they could stand in the ditch bottom wearing crutch high, thigh boots whilst holding their feet in the energy sucking mud along the bed of the dyke, and remove a layer of silt with a copper tipped wooden shovel called a 'sluff',.

Hydraulically powered, tractor mounted, flail hedging machines can do as much work in a day now, as it would have taken one man half a winter, and ditching is now done by contractors using tracked hydraulic machines incorporating a six foot wide bucket.

The dramatic effects of mechanisation, that had started in the fifties, rapidly gained momentum until by 1970s; a full blown agricultural revolution was taking place. The centuries old traditional fair of hiring farm labour in Louth Market Place on Candlemas Day,(2nd February) for the new farm year commencing on the following April 6th would shortly be condemned to the pages of history. It used to be an important date in a farm labourer's year when they had an opportunity to meet rarely seen colleagues and swap experiences as they sought a a new employer. 'Flitting day' on April 6th was a time of mass migration between farms when the new hired labour and their families were conveyed with all their worldly goods, by tractor and trailer, or in earlier times by horse and cart to the new tied house vacated earlier that morning by the departing family.

The changes that were occurring meant that farmers with only a small acreage decided as they neared retirement, they would sell their outlying fields to nearby larger farmers. Many of their much smaller fields comprising only an acre or so in area, that generally fronted a public road within the main block of the village proved to have a much higher value as building plots for the more mobile town dwellers, who wanted to live in the country. At a time when a decent sized house could be built for £3,000, quite large plots were selling within the main body of the village during the early sixties for £350 to £400 each,.

Farm workers reaching retirement age, along with younger workers who found better paid factory work on Louth's new industrial estates, contributed to the rapid reduction in farm labour as increased mechanisation gathered pace. Consequently, many of the tied cottages, that were now no longer required, were sold off cheaply to the new villagers who no longer earned a living from agriculture but merely wanted to enjoy the peace and tranquillity of the countryside. The seventies and eighties ushered in a completely new type of villager, with many people lacking allegiance to traditional elements of village and country life that for generations had been a cornerstone of rural communities. Many of the newcomers came from an urban background in the south of England, and found that they could purchase a great deal more for their money up here, particularly as most folk wanted to retire or discover a safe environment to exercise their dogs in the countryside.

Following the demise of the majority of the quite small acreage farmers, (mentioned earlier) of perhaps, up to twenty acres, in the nineteen forties, the nineteen fifties and early sixties saw the decline of farms up to one hundred acres, as they could no longer generate sufficient capital to invest in more modern technologies.

During the nineteen seventies there was a major move to specialise, with many farms of less than two hundred acres now finding it difficult to be viable as a truly mixed farm, and not large enough to warrant the investment of a purely arable unit.

Dairy farming in the village, by the 1980s, was reduced to two large dairy herds employing full time milkmen to look after their Friesian/ Holstein herds, and one small specialist father and son farm milking Jersey cows.

Our farm uniquely still retained its large pedigree, beef cattle herd, having dispersed the flock of sheep in 1970. It was a time when there was a big swing away from livestock enterprisers in the eastern counties, as farmers shed labour and concentrated on growing crops by using ever larger more sophisticated machinery. Many farmers, at this time, because of tighter economic conditions sold their land to institutional buyers or pension funds and immediately rented the land back thus freeing up capital to invest in better buildings and equipment.

Major changes took place in the 1960's and 70's when grant aided, land drainage schemes were carried out by land drainage contractors such as Vickers from Saltfleetby, who used special tracked 'gripping machines' that not only cut a four to five feet deep trench, but laid a continuous line of 12 inch long, clay pipes, with a 3 inch internal diameter, that were superseded in the 1980s by plastic piping. The slight gap between the clay pipes as they butted up to each other and the very small slits in the plastic pipes provided an entry for water to enter the drain which was further aided by providing a porous fill of about eighteen inches of stone placed directly over the line of pipes.

Conscience Hill was under drained in 1970 when the overgrown hedges were removed to provide unrestricted access in order that an elaborate herring bone network of underground pipes could be installed. These were connected to a series of larger pipes called outfalls that evacuated the water into the surrounding Monks Dyke. This type of drainage was carried out in all our arable fields over a seventeen year period from 1960 to 1977, enabling crops to be grown in fields that hitherto would have been too waterlogged for the production of arable crops.

Aerial photograph showing the herring bone lines of fields being under drained. Note also Louth Park Abbey, lower left. Conscience Hill, left of centre. Cockerington Hall, right of centre.

In the late 1940's the farm purchased its first of several grey 25 hp petrol/paraffin engined Ferguson tractors, at a time when the predominant tractors to be found on British farms were Standard Fords or the newer dark blue, Fordson Majors. On a good day, a Ferguson tractor with its hydraulically mounted two furrow plough could plough three to four acres, but by the 1970's tractor size had increased to 60 to 80 h.p, so that a Massey Ferguson 65 tractor, of that period pulling a mounted four furrow plough could plough as much as ten acres in a day. Today our 300 h.p. Massey Ferguson tractor, pulling a massive seven furrow reversible plough, is capable of ploughing forty acres plus on a good day. Driver comfort has changed beyond all recognition, over the intervening fifty years, moving from the time that the tractor driver sat astride the gearbox on those early grey Fergies finding little comfort from a hard pan shaped metal seat. During the winter months it was necessary to wear an ex-army great coat to keep warm and place a folded sack bag over the knees to keep legs dry.

The first tractor cabs that came on the market in the mid 1960s were highly regarded, even though they were very rudimentary, compared to today's cabs. A metal frame was covered in canvas with a glass windscreen and a roll up plastic rear window secured with press studs. Today's tractors are as comfortable as most modern cars, with air conditioning, stereo radios, power steering, and arm chair type seating, plus an excellent array of lights for working after dark.

In spite of driving a tractor with more than 9 times the horse power, at 225 hp, compared to those 25 hp grey Fergies of 60 years ago, the 4 wheels of my tractor, duelled up with 4 more wheels give a wide weight distribution that ensures minimum damage is done to soil structure by this much heavier machine.

Lindsey Marsh Drainage Board. Demonstration of drainage past and present, February 2011. This is how farm workers would have dressed in the years following the second world war. Note: The ex-army great coats tied with binder twine.

Cropping patterns have changed radically over the years as specialisation and larger farms has resulted in more sophisticated mechanisation which in turn has accelerated the exodus of farm labour. Improved varieties of cereals have been produced by the plant breeders which are not only high yielding but have a much shorter straw length enabling autumn planting to commence much earlier. The area of land devoted to spring oats has reduced sharply, particularly as they were very prone to 'lodge' (the long straw made the crop vulnerable to bad weather when they could be blown flat), making them extremely difficult to harvest as crops laid flat on the ground soon start to sprout. The demand for low cholesterol, vegetable oil saw the introduction in the late 1960's of the yellow flowering oil seed rape crops, which in addition to being a break crop from cereals is now an important cash crop in its own right as it rapidly replaced the traditional break of a red clover, rye grass mixture. Oil seed rape has a very long growing season so an additional benefit is that it helps the seasonal work load by sowing the new crop towards the end of August on land that's been cleared of winter barley. Rape is harvested, at about the same time as winter barley, in late July, so its other important advantage is that it spreads the harvest and allows the land to be cultivated in preparation for winter wheat.

In the 1950's it proved almost impossible to control many broad leaved weeds and persistent grasses in cereal crops when it became a common sight at harvest time to see great beds of prickly green thistles and waving heads of wild oats, standing above the ears of corn. However over the subsequent years agro chemical companies have made rapid strides in developing sprays that can control many of these troublesome weeds. Fungicides now combat many of the fungal diseases that had previously decimated crops, and insecticides can now kill plagues of insects such as aphids.

Towards the end of the 1970s manufacturers such as Sanderson at Skegness introduced the first industrial type of masted forklifts that were fitted to the three point linkage on the back of tractors which had the ability to lift much more weight, higher than the fore end loaders. This was a big improvement on the original font end loader as the forklift could lift a half ton bucket of grain from a floor grain store, over the side of a bulk grain lorry. A little later Sandersons developed the teleporters with their extending booms that enabled this new breed of machines to both lift and reach. Major changes occurred when Britain joined the Common Market in 1971 and the farm deficiency payment scheme, that had served the country so well for a generation was abandoned.

A new generation of politicians with little practical knowledge of Britain's War time food shortages and rationing were determined to forge an economic union of the principle war time antagonists in order to prevent future European wars. In that context, potential consumer food price hikes, were certainly preferable to wartime destruction.

The European Economic Community, or the Common Market as it was then known, had a combined population of two hundred and forty million people, whose market was then controlled by export and import tariffs. Inevitably as production increased with most commodities above world prices surpluses accrued, leading to the so-called Grain, Beef and Butter Mountains alongside the lakes of wine and milk.

The five giant redundant aircraft hangers at nearby Manby were taken over by the Intervention Board, in common with many other large buildings throughout Europe, to store purchased grain, which was sold off cheaply several years later onto the world market. The Intervention Board, by the use of import and export tariffs, strictly controlled the market, preventing high prices occurring in times of world shortage.

By the 1990s capital grants had disappeared and 'set aside' was introduced taking up to 10% of productive land out of cropping. Finally, cattle and sheep headage payments were replaced in 2004 with the new Single Farm Payment when a proportion of support monies were then diverted to environmental projects. Grass margins surrounding arable fields, replanting of hedges and conservation in general is now widely encouraged.

CHAPTER 12
The Best Laid Plans!

If I had gazed east towards the marsh and the coast from this spot in the summer months of the 1960's, I would have been able to see as many as 40 yearling Lincoln Red heifers contentedly grazing, the 26 acre, grass field part of Conscience Hill, below me. If I looked a little further beyond the field towards the village I would have seen even more fields filled with grazing cattle or sheep, but now most of those fields are ploughed and growing arable crops.

The Lincoln Red cattle would have formed a part of our six hundred strong pedigree herd, with the very best young bulls being sold to other breeding herds in eastern England and Scotland, though the majority of the annual output was sold as commercial fat stock through the local cattle market at Louth.

A pedigree Lincoln Red Bull Show and Sale was held at Louth Cattle Market on the second Tuesday in February. I remember that it invariably coincided with one of the coldest periods of the winter as snow frequently whitened the ground.

The Lincoln Bull Fair was a much grander affair, held over two days, at Lincolns Carholme racecourse. It was originally held in early April to coincide with the big April Fair held on the south common. In later years when the demand for Lincoln Red bulls declined the date was brought forward to early March and the venue was changed to the Lincolnshire showground.

One of Harvey's cattle wagons painted in the fleets dark green livery with the name of its Louth depot prominently displayed on the headboard above the cab, would pull into our farmyard just as dawn was breaking to take our bulls. We liked to leave home quite early on the Wednesday morning with the 6 or 7 bulls that we generally took to Lincoln, in order that we had adequate time to prepare the bulls for show later that day. Preparation for the event however had commenced months earlier when the bulls were broken in and trained to lead on an halter, which was followed by a rigorous regime of washing and grooming and extensive walking exercise at the end of an halter. I remember that originally we used to transport the bulls by tying them by their halters in a continuous line to the side of the lorry in order that they kept reasonably clean, until one memorable occasion when one of them stepped over another's halter and hung himself. We had stopped as usual to inspect them at Hainton, which was a midway point on the hour long journey when we discovered the tragedy. It was with some difficulty that we pulled the dead bull out of the lorry on to the roadside verge where we cut his throat with a pocket knife in order that the blood would drain from him, so that his carcase could be collected and transferred to a slaughter house in Louth.

After that they were always tied line abreast facing forward.

Upon arrival at Lincoln racecourse we were allocated horse boxes where we would not only house the bulls but where we also lived and slept for the next two days. Food was packed up before leaving home and a big, hessian, beet pulp bag was selected, cleaned and prepared as a sleeping bag. During the 1950s before the breed declined in numbers, more than 300 Lincoln Red bulls would be shown and judged in different

Louth bull fair 1959. Judges, Dick Bee and Jim Ranby inspecting J G Needham and sons bull held by their herdsman Charlie Lambert.

129

Exercising a team of 7 bulls for Lincoln bull fair 1970. L-R Keith Mathewson, Tony Mathewson, Bill Mathewson, Malcolm Mathewson, my father, self.

age classes. Lincoln Bull Fair concluded with an auction the following day. After the show the bulls were fed and watered, and those of us who were sleeping with the bulls overnight walked into Lincoln to watch wrestling in the Drill Hall, which at the time, was a new craze sweeping Britain.

The next show and sale took place in Boston, on the first Monday in May where it was held within the cattle market pens in Bargate. I remember that we were always surrounded by frenetic activity as the travelling Fair had just transferred from Lincoln. This was never a particularly good sale, as most farmers had already selected their new bull at earlier sales. I always remember this as being one of the first warm days of summer when I would invariably see the first new potatoes appearing through the ground at Sibsey on our journey to Boston.

The last sale of the year was held in a grass paddock off Park lane in Alford, during the first week in November. In contrast to the fine summery weather in Boston it always seemed to rain on Alford bull fair making a miserable wet early winter's day as coats soon became saturated with trickles of rain running off soaked flat caps and finding a drain down shirt collars. Bull Calves that had been born that spring were always a feature of Alfords sale, with the late Guy Mountain of Tothill regularly bringing a strong representation. Some of the yearling bulls, that had won awards at the summer shows, were also sold to good effect through the portable ring that Dickenson, Davey and Markham along with Simons of Boston brought to the sale. After Alford Bull sale we turned our attention to preparing fat stock animals for the Christmas fatstock shows commencing with the Smithfield show held in London's, Earls Court during the first week of December, followed by the local fat stock shows at Louth and Alford. For many years ending in 1979 we generally entered 4 or 5 Lincoln Reds in the Smithfield Breed classes and 3 or 4 Charolais cross Lincolns in the carcass classes. Carcass cattle were judged alive on the Sunday, after which they were taken away for slaughter, in order that they could return as carcases, to be judged for carcass composition on the following Wednesday morning. Our most notable success in the competition came in 1978 when we showed four steers that were each awarded a first prize, in their respective classes as live animals, followed, by one of them taking the supreme championship award for live animals. On their return the carcases were judged by another judge, who gave our animals three more first prizes and a second in addition to selecting two of the carcasses for the champion and reserve champion carcase. We were presented with the gold challenge cup by the Queen Mother. Following the sale on the Wednesday, most of us returned home that night except

Alford bull fair November 1959, self with a team of our three bulls.

131

one man who would come home on the Thursday night with some of the cattle that had been purchased by local butchers to be slaughtered much closer to Christmas. Sleeping arrangements were pretty basic, as everyone slept on iron bedsteads in large communal halls in the basement of Earls Court. It was always very difficult sleeping down there under the bright electric lights, as people were constantly laughing and talking, with many of them moving around throughout the night when any sound seemed to be magnified as it echoed from the large concrete walls and pillars.

Perhaps because of the atmosphere and lack of sleep we always seemed to develop colds on our return to Lincolnshire. In later years I used to stop at the West Centre Hotel nearby, parking the car in the underground car park and then walking to the show each day

On one unforgettable occasion one of our prize winning Lincoln red steers had been purchased by Lakings of Louth, and had returned back to the farm for delivery to their slaughter house in Eve Street in the week following Christmas.

It was my job to take the steer into Louth, as I had previously done on countless other occasions, using the Landrover and trailer. Bearing in mind that this was a particularly quiet animal that had been halter trained and led around the show ring in London among crowds of people, there was no indication that this was going to be anything other than a simple routine operation. I backed the trailer, as usual, within the abattoirs big outer doors, and opened the lairage gates in order that I could drop the trailer door and drive the steer inside one of the pens. The first part of the operation went quite according to plan, but then just as I was about to shut the lairage gate behind the steer, he gave a snort and with an almighty lunge burst through the gate and galloped in a maddened frenzy across the small inner yard and crammed himself through an open door into a small toilet cubicle. Reversing out of the toilet he rolled his eyes and snorted once again, then with eyes blazing and head held high he briefly looked at the pair of 8ft high outer doors, before rushing towards them when he almost succeeded in jumping over them, but the sheer power of his momentum smashed them wide open allowing him to run at a frenzied gallop in the direction of Charles Street pond and a residential part of the town. As nobody else was working at the slaughter house at the time, I gave chase on foot following the animal as he surged through gardens and fences to emerge on High Holme road. By this time the placid steer,

132

that I had so recently loaded from his stable at home was totally enraged as he galloped as fast as his legs could carry him towards the County Hospital. However he was running too fast to negotiate the right turn into the entrance, so with feet slithering and sliding on the smooth tarmac road surface he careered down the hill to the Grimsby road where he was confronted by traffic approaching from both directions.

In the meantime I realised that I was rapidly losing ground as I breathlessly gave chase some 50 yards or so behind him it dawned on me that perhaps he had an inkling of what lay behind the green doors he had an even greater so he had good reason for running faster than me. Presumably he must have realised that this journey had a one way only ticket and he wouldn't be returning home again once those doors were closed behind him. With cars and lorries spooking him, he turned right on to the A16 and continued his frenzied gallop up Grimsby hill leading out of the town. He was uncertain whether to charge cars or skittishly shy past them. Towards the top of the hill he was confronted by yet another approaching vehicle whose driver in a state of panic stopped in the middle of the road, when he saw a wild animal with flaring nostrils, dribbling white froth from its mouth running up the hill towards him. Uncertain what he should do next, the steer abruptly veered to the right and surged down a house drive to emerge under a line of washing blowing in the wind in the back garden of a house on the south side of North Holme road. Flapping white sheets seemed to infuriate him further causing him to shy away and barge through the wooden fence of the next door garden where she was confronted by a lady pinning out her smalls on a clothes line erected over her back lawn. She shrieked and ran for the safety of her back door as the animal ploughed headlong through the next series of gardens, running amok through other lines of washing that Monday morning. The steer showed no respect for lawns, flower borders or vegetable patches as he ploughed on regardless, in his desperation to escape all of the obstacles that seemed to be placed in his way. Finally, by now, completely maddened he emerged once again from the gardens onto High Holme road and crossed over into a fuel depot where I temporally lost sight of him among an array of fuel tanks. This gave me my first opportunity to breathlessly ask one of the curious crowd who had emerged from houses behind me, if they would kindly phone my home number with a request for urgent assistance. The steer now breathing almost as heavily as I was stood for a few seconds with head held aloft as he scanned his surroundings then with wild staring eyes and heaving sides continued to pant and snort as he careered into Kenneth Wilsons agricultural merchants yard and lost himself amongst stacks of palletised fertiliser. When help finally arrived from the farm they brought with them a couple of cows that pacified the steer sufficiently to enable us to reload him in the trailer and successfully transport the now much calmer animal to the slaughter house. This episode illustrates quite graphically how, what would normally be quite a simple routine exercise in moving stock, could suddenly take a totally unexpected turn with far reaching consequences, as I was to discover as I started to deliver bulls pretty well all over the country.

Towards the end of the 1960's and even more during the 1970's demand for our Lincoln Red bulls declined dramatically as the market for what were then described as "continentals" rapidly gained momentum.

By the late 60s whilst I was still looking after the commercial sheep flock I was also increasingly responsible for the pedigree cattle side of the business as my father was happy to pass some of the responsibility over to me. I soon realised that it took little more effort to get a reluctant calf to suck its mother than a lamb, with the calf having a vastly different final value. With the decline in local demand for Lincoln Red bulls I found that I had to look for markets in other parts of the country, and in doing so established a personal delivery service linked to private on farm sales. With the introduction of the first French Charolais cattle into the UK during the 1960's, the fierce patriotic loyalty and allegiance to traditional British beef breeds started to break down. Thus it was that Lincoln Reds broke out of their County boundaries and were accepted with other beef breeds at Perth, Hawick and St Boswell auction sales, even though the Aberdeen Angus and Beef Shorthorns breed societies did their utmost to prevent the introduction of other cattle breeds into their traditional fiefdom of Scotland.

Lincoln Reds, perhaps because of their Shorthorn ancestry, but certainly inspired by the breeds pioneering work in weight recording came to the attention of Mr Colin Ball. At that time he was attached to the Scottish Agricultural colleges, and instantly became a convert to the breed when he started to visit Lincoln Red herds in Lincolnshire and particularly our farm on a regular basis to purchase bulls for farmers throughout the north of Scotland. So began an interesting episode in my life when I made a great many journeys to northern Scotland taking bulls to some very remote locations. I recall that one of my very first long journeys was one of some 1200 miles. It took me 4 days to make the round trip delivering a bull with our Landrover and trailer, to the harbour at Scrabster near Thurso for onward shipment to a remote island in the Orkneys.

Diesel Landrovers were pretty basic in those days with few creature comforts such as a heater. Car heaters, particularly in commercial vehicles such as Landrovers, were considered only for wimps. The unlined, metal roof constantly dripped water if there was any change in the external temperature, whilst the poorly fitting doors drummed and vibrated, consequently making the vehicle extremely noisy, as it struggled to go much faster than 40 miles an hour. The body of our 10 feet long by 6 feet wide cattle trailer had been constructed by Len Pridgeon, (the Great Carlton joiner), of ¾ inch thick marine ply, supported on a low slung axel, by a pair of ex army balloon tyres that tended to go flat with great regularity. Although I carried a spare wheel, it was rather exceptional if I didn't get a flat tyre on one of the longer trips, which had me on tenterhooks for the remainder of the journey with no spare left. Looking back over all the years that I've taken cattle around the country, I suppose it's always the things that go wrong that I tend to remember, rather than all the other trips that were uneventful.

I vividly remember the occasion when I was taking two $2\frac{1}{2}$ year old bulls that must have weighed at least a ton each to a farm near Melton Mowbray, using the trailer with balloon tyres. Driving along the busy Newark Rd in North Hykeham, just outside Lincoln, I heard a bang that sounded like an explosion. The trailer swerved sharply to the right with a hail of sparks coming from the offside trailer wheel. I had a puncture! The difficulty with that type of balloon tyre, was that in the event of a puncture the axle dropped to the road, making it quite impossible to move the trailer onto the roadside. As heavy lorries thundered past, within inches of my feet, I managed to jack up the trailer by means of a hydraulic jack and lots of pieces of wood, until I could eventually change the wheel with my spare and resume my journey towards Melton Mowbray.

On the long stretch of road beyond the Bingham roundabout, my worst fears were confounded when I suffered yet another puncture, except on this occasion I was partially prepared for the inevitable bang.

I was left with little alternative other than to flag down a lorry to take me and the punctured wheel to the nearest garage and hope that they could repair it.

After travelling some considerable distance in the direction of Leicester with my wheel in the cab of a helpful lorry driver, I succeeded in finding a garage that managed to effect a temporary repair by applying a gaiter to the inside wall of the tyre and mending the puncture. Returning to my vehicle via the kind generosity of another lorry driver with the wheel repaired I found that the wheel I had changed in Lincoln was now also flat.

My only option was to get it repaired, but unfortunately it had developed a hole in the tyres wall that would have required an even larger gaiter, so it was clearly out of the question to complete my journey even if I had managed to get it repaired. That left me with no alternative other than to get to a phone box, and to phone up a transport company in the Melton Mowbray area to come and pick up the two bulls. I could then limp down to Melton Mowbray and make a much more permanent repair to the two tyres that I had.

I seem to have had a lot of bad luck with that particular trailer because I remember on yet another occasion Mr Dick Marshall from Welton le Wold had bought a bull from us early one May. As this was quite a short journey from Cockerington to Welton le Wold I arranged to meet Mr Marshall at his farm when I agreed to drop the bull into a field of grazing cows and calves.

The trailer was equipped with a small side door on its front offside for getting inside the trailer to remove a bull's halter and lead rein that was clipped into his ring. It was essential, in the interests of stability that the single axle trailer was loaded heavier to the front in order that it would place more weight on the Land Rover drawbar, which consequently meant that bulls had to be tied to the front of the trailer.

In spite of the fact that I had carried out this procedure many times in the past I found that on this occasion, when I attempted to remove the bull's halter and lead rein that the animal gave a snort and snatched the rope out of my hand as he squeezed his body through the side door before I could manage to close it. Something must have spooked him because he was perfectly quiet at home. With his halter and lead rein now dangling between his front feet the bull couldn't help but step on the lead rein, which instantly gave a sharp tug on the sensitive part of his nose. In attempting to escape the pain, he broke into a gallop which only resulted in the sequence of stepping on the rope occurring more frequently, and that had the effect of making him run all the faster. Rather than head towards a herd of cows and calves at the far end of the field that might well have pacified him, the by now enraged animal racing at full tilt ploughed through a barbed wire fence and thorn hedge that bordered the field. He then disappeared from sight into a large field of spring barley that stretched way out of sight down the valley in front of me. My next glimpse of him was charging across another field on the opposite side of the valley with his head held high as he passed through more hedges and fields of growing crops. It was about that time that I became seriously worried as to what might happen next with a maddened bull on the rampage, as visions of him injuring someone started to fill my mind with dread.

By late afternoon following a great deal of frantic chasing across large Wold arable fields with a number of Mr Marshalls aged farm workers walking hesitantly in the rear, we eventually succeeded in finding the bull. Gently we coaxed him back to the original field, where we reunited him with the cows and calves in order that we could bring all of the cattle into an adjacent crew yard, where I was able to remove his halter and lead rein. This was most certainly, not the best way to impress a new buyer and to convince him about the quality and quietness of our cattle.

In January 1965 Mr Colin Ball accompanied by Mr Sandy Lee, from Fraserborough on the north east coast of Aberdeenshire came down to the farm and purchased a couple of pedigree Lincoln Red heifers. So towards the end of that month, I optimistically, in view of my previous experience with punctures on the old trailer, loaded the two heifers on to a brand new trailer that we'd purchased a couple of months earlier at Smithfield show from Ifor Williams.

The name of Ifor Williams is now as synonymous with livestock trailers as Hoover is to vacuum cleaners, but the trailer that we had purchased all those years ago was one of the very first trailers that he had built. As he had been exhibiting it at the Smithfield Show in London, it was unsurprising that Ifor Williams personally delivered it to us on his return to North Wales.

The shiny silver aluminium panelled body with twin wheels mounted under the chassis looked incredibly smart compared to the faded green paint of our old wooden trailer with its fat balloon wheels positioned midway on either side of the trailer I was soon to discover however that the tyres Ifor Williams had fitted to his trailer were meant for vehicles travelling quite short distances and were not particularly suited for long distance roadwork as they soon became hot. Mr Williams in those early pioneering days was unsure where his main market lay. So in order that he could produce a multi use trailer, he made one that in addition to being suitable to transport cattle and sheep would be high enough to transport horses. I soon discovered that the 12 foot long by 6 foot wide, 7 feet high trailer, gave too much wind resistance. A trailer a foot lower would be quiet high enough for transporting cattle.

I made an early start at 5.30 am and soon met frequent snow showers carried along on a biting, north east wind. In spite of being very cold I got as far as Arbroath that evening, arriving in the town just after 5pm and found a bleak hotel overlooking the sea, for my nights stay. As I was the only guest in the hotel, I dined alone in a large cold restaurant, to the sound of waves crashing on the rocks below, and a banshee wind howling and tearing at the gable end of the hotel. I spent a sleepless night so it was with some trepidation that I stepped out of the hotel the following morning to continue my journey north along the bleak exposed Aberdeenshire coast. The north easterly wind had increased in strength to gale force overnight, and was now making driving very difficult. The windscreen wipers on my Land Rover struggled to deflect the constant bombardment of snow from the frequent blizzard like snow showers. I don't think that I once got out of third gear for the total duration of the journey until I finally turned into Mr Lees farm yard in the early afternoon and off loaded the heifers into a covered yard.

Accepting Mr & Mrs Lee's kind offer of lunch, I was never the less anxious to get on the road again and travel down to Arbroath before the drifting snows closed the roads completely, and isolated me in North East Scotland. Unfortunately, as I was about to set off I found that one of the small tyres on the new trailer was flat, and as I didn't carry a spare at that stage, I had to quickly make arrangements for a company in Fraserburgh to get a replacement tyre from Turriff where the snow was much worse. After the new tyre was fitted I finally set off at dusk encountering a very difficult journey through snow as I retraced my journey south. I was conscious that there was a very real danger of the trailer jack knifing so I consequently travelled very slowly, rarely exceeding 20 mph through the driving snow on roads that were extremely slippery. The storm had created a power cut over a very large area of Aberdeenshire making it quite late by the time I arrived back at my Hotel in Arbroath when thankfully the remainder of the journey home, whilst difficult, was largely uneventful.

We only kept that trailer for a year as the 7 foot height that would have been brilliant for horses was of little benefit for carrying cattle. The extra foot of unnecessary height created too much wind resistance so that all of our subsequent trailers have only been 6 foot high. From the mid 60s to the late 70s I made that journey on many occasions, and as I became more familiar with the road, I found that I could travel considerably further in a day, eventually making my first overnight stop just south of Inverness.

Beef recording was the initiative of the Lincoln Red Cattle Society who pioneered weight recording using adjusted periodic weights, ranging from one to six hundred day intervals that for the very first time gave buyers a measurable comparison between animals. Unfortunately during the 1960s medical concerns regarding the undesirability of eating saturated animal fats, along with the rise of the supermarkets and their pre-packaged meats, started to change eating patterns. The era of cheap air travel which led to the general public travelling from these shores for the first time on package holidays introduced the general public to completely different tastes of food, which all contributed to the desirability for leaner meat.

By 1965 the domestic U.K. pedigree, cattle, breed societies who had traditionally exerted enormous political pressure on the exclusivity of British breeds resulting in the title of "The World's stock yard" were coming under increasing pressure. There was a desire to improve British Breeds quickly with different genetics, that would allow cattle to grow quicker and leaner. Intensive Government lobbying by a group of mainly dairy farmers led by the late Tony Harman from Chesham in Buckinghamshire were successful in enabling the Milk Marketing Board, who then had a near monopoly in the sale of semen to import the first Charolais Bulls from France in 1962 for strictly controlled evaluation purposes. As only bulls could be imported at that time, those early pioneers formed the British Charolais Cattle Society and started a grading up programme. The goal of 31/32 pure blood to become 'British Pedigree Charolais', was to follow five successive crossings back to a full pedigree Charolais Bull. Alex Anderson, a well known Shorthorn breeder noted that "French Charolais" have got everything that the British Breeds have lost – size and growth rate with meat in all the right places". So successful were these first cross calves that the Government gave way and allowed the first importation in 1965 of two hundred heifers. Following quarantine in France and the U.K, they successfully passed a series of very stringent health tests. Immediately there was a ready market for females in this country stimulated by demand from overseas

Conscience Hill

countries that hitherto could not import directly from France. However the insatiable demand for females was controlled by the quarantine facilities in the U.K. which had a limit of two hundred per year.

We were among the early group of pedigree beef breeders who recognised the attributes of the Charolais breed of cattle, so that in the absence of being able to purchase pure bred Charolais females, decided to AI a batch of our Lincoln Red cows to one of the Milk Marketing boards imported AI Charolais Bulls from France and embark on a grading up programme. The first cross calves were a distinctive ginger colour, though after crossing that cross and the following cross back to a full French bull the resultant third cross calves were completely white. We soon discovered that these Charolais cross Lincoln Red cattle not only grew well, but had outstanding fleshing characteristics of "lean meat in all the right places".

As a long established Lincoln Red Breeder with many years on the Lincoln Red Council, in addition to being a past Lincoln Red Society President with years of experience as a cattle Judge, my Father added a note of caution by very sensibly pointing out, "If Charolais Cattle were any good they would have been here before now". At that time it would have taken the sale of twenty Lincoln Red Heifers to purchase one Charolais heifer of the same age, - a powerful argument for proceeding with caution.

In spite of that I gladly accepted an invitation by The British Charolais Cattle Society to go to France on one of the early buying commissions to spend a week in western and central France purchasing cattle from some of the very best herds on behalf of the Society members, to help fill the overwhelming demand.

At that time such was the demand for females it was necessary to hold a ballot, among society members, to select the two hundred successful breeders who would participate in the final draw at the Dundee Quarantine Station. During their evaluation of all the animals on the first day, the two hundred breeders assembled there, were invited to place the animals in preference from one to two hundred. On the second day the names of the breeders were drawn from a rotating drum and had to quickly nominate their chosen animal, as they needed to keep eliminating animals that other breeders had selected from their list. In spite of going to France on the buying commission I was never the less fortunate enough to be one of the two hundred lucky breeders to obtain a place in the draw. Luckily my favourite animal Julie, that I had seen and participated in

Cockerington Baron sold to the Milk Marketing Board in 1988, one of our most famous Charolais bulls.

buying in the Vendee, was still available when my name at number sixty seven was drawn. Julie produced many outstanding animals during her breeding life culminating in breeding an outstanding bull named Cockerington Baron who firmly established the Cockerington prefix as a leading pedigree Charolais Herd. We purchased an exceptionally tall bull named Mountpleasant Rockford, who was Barons sire, from the late Willie Whitelaws award winning Mountpleasant herd at Perth. So given the fact that both Barons sire and dam were outstanding animals it was perhaps little wonder that Baron had the distinction of recording the highest four hundred day weight of any weight recorded animal in the U.K.at that time. He scaled a massive 840 kilograms or 1848 lbs, that was substantially better than any weights that we had achieved with our Lincoln Reds. Baron was sold to the Milk Marketing Board from where his semen was sold worldwide producing, progeny that dominated pedigree show awards for many years.

The sale of Baron almost ended in tragedy however. By the July he had successfully passed all of his tests following a lengthy period in quarantine on the farm. As we waited the time when the MMB would collect him he was housed in an adjacent pen to two other bulls, seperated by a stout 5 barred gate. Hearing a disturbance from the bull pens one Friday afternoon we discovered that somehow Baron had pushed his head through the narrow gaps between the bars in the gate where it became wedged fast. The other bulls thought this was great fun as they fought his head and smashed the front of his jaw. Fortunately our vet Andrew

Cook worked wonders by wiring the jaw together. After much care Baron recovered and passed all his tests once more.

Over the course of the next few years our Lincoln Red Herd declined as Charolais numbers increased, resulting in the last of the Red cattle leaving the farm in 1985 to be replaced entirely by white Charolais. Over the intervening years the Cockerington Charolais Herd prefix has become synonymous with easy calving and good temperament, coupled with length, smooth fleshing, and good bone structure on well positioned legs.

Today practically all our cattle are sold for breeding, with bulls going into pedigree herds or used as terminal sires in commercial herds. Females provide foundation animals for the establishment of new pedigree herds throughout the country. Semen from Cockerington bulls is now widely used throughout the world, in countries as diverse as Mexico, Brazil, Ireland, Germany and Norway. Our Charolais *polling programme started entirely by accident as a direct consequence of using a Full French horned Charolais bull over some of our Poll Lincoln Red cows. The initial batch of cows were artificially inseminated in order that their female offspring could form the original grade A foundation animals, but had only been selected on the basis that they had calved during a certain period. Inevitably there were a proportion of poll cows amongst them as we had only started using a heterozygous poll Lincoln Red bull alongside horned bulls a few years earlier. (Heterozygous means that the poll factor is not 100% poll as a bull will only leave about half poll calves when mated with a horned female).

So it was with a fair degree of luck that a very good completely white poll bull calf was born to a three quarter or grade B cow, that we named, Cockerington Majestic, and he proved to be the foundation for our Charolais Polling programme. Three successive sons, each one better than his father were used over either full French cows or various grades, when it then became imperative that other blood lines had to be used to prevent in breeding.

In 1984 a Poll Charolais bull named Val End Commander was imported from Canada by a consortium of breeders, which led to Robert Needham from Gayton le Wold and ourselves jointly purchasing one of his sons called Penny-parc Raglan who had been Poll Champion bull in Perth. Not long afterwards further Canadian poll blood was added with the purchase of Cullum Matador who was also sired by a Canadian poll bull.

In order to improve quality we made a decision to divide our herd into two portions, breeding one half to a succession of very well bred horn bulls, with the female progeny being served by a direct line of Cockerington poll bulls commencing with a son of Matador called Cockerington Impressive, who in turn was superseded by one of his sons called Cockerington Lion, and then by one of his sons named Cockerington Roman.

The female progeny from each of these respective crossings went across to the other side of the herd, to be out crossed by a succession of high quality horned sires. The object from the earliest days has been to ensure that the essential attributes of good temperament and easy calving linked to size, bone structure, and good legs wasn't sacrificed in a premature attempt to poll the herd too quickly. Consequently it has taken many years of careful selection to produce uniformity in the herd which has now allowed us to move on to the next stage by using fresh lines of stock bulls so that almost all calves are now natural polls.

In July 2008 we made a significant step forward by importing a poll Charolais bull called Nyas Carlson from Anders Wiklert in Sweden.

*Poll - Means the cattle are naturally hornless.

Cockerington Brookside exported to South Africa

143

Exhibiting one of our Charolais steers at Louth Fatstock show 1986.

CHAPTER 13
Up and Down

Following my return from New Zealand in 1962 I thought that my association with the YFC would soon end as I was approaching 25 which at that time was the upper age limit. However I first had to visit many of the clubs throughout Lincolnshire and adjacent counties to give illustrated talks on my experiences. Over the next two years I must have delivered well over 100 talks to not only YFCs, but also to many other organisations throughout the area.

In the autumn of 1962 I was honoured to be elected county YFC vice chairman, a position that I held for two years before serving another two years as county chairman. I felt that over the previous ten years I had much to thank the organisation for because after all, it was through the YFC that I had just spent over 8 months travelling quite literally around the world by sea. The movement had given me the confidence to speak in public without any inhibitions about addressing any audience, and in addition I had learned a whole raft of farming skills, receiving a gold badge as a testament to becoming proficient in a wide range of crafts ranging from veterinary skills to hedge laying.

Above all I had an extremely happy social life making many close friends that have lasted a lifetime. It was perhaps inevitably that the movement would be instrumental in my meeting my future wife Pat towards the end of 1962 when we became engaged to be married a year later at Christmas 1963, and planned our wedding for the autumn of 1964. As there were no available empty houses on the farm at that time it was decided to build a new house mid way between my old home at Hill House Farm and South View Farm. Tradesmen who worked on a regular basis on the farm were employed enabling the property to be completed in just 14 weeks from the time that the first turf was cut in early March to completion at the end of June. So well did the house building go that we decided to bring the wedding foreword to mid July in order that it didn't conflict with harvest or clash with the YFC Autumn County Rally that was being held at Hill House Farm in October of that year, when I had been appointed Rally chairman. As the 60s decade passed into the70s both my father and uncle became semi retired, and although they continued to take a keen interest they played little part in the day to day running of the farm.

My wife Pat produced three bright healthy children commencing with Sally in September1965, then Alistair in April 1968 followed by Andrea in August 1969. Pat actively supported them through their school years and then in her capacity as guide leader provided active encouragement for the girls to maximise their full potential through the guiding movement.

Family photograph 2007 - Back Row: Sharon and Alistair, son and daughter in law, Andrea and Andrew, daughter and son in law, Sally and Stuart, daughter and son in law. Middle Row: Olivia, Harry, Alfred, Pat, myself and Eleanor. Front Row: James, Oliver and Jospeh

The family company at that time comprised apart from me, my father and uncle as the two senior partners, along with my cousin John who was 7 years older than me.

Pat and I rounding Cape Horn in 2007 on Swan Hellenic Minerva II

There are many advantages of larger farm units, of which more acres is an obvious example, as it means that the business can make a better utilisation of machinery. The capital cost is spread over a greater area avoiding the duplication that would be experienced by the same acreage divided into smaller units. Then of course there is the benefit of more managers as there is always someone on call which removes the tied aspect so frequently experienced on smaller farms. However there are disadvantages, the major one being of obtaining agreement from all the partners if a change in policy is to be adopted as the consensus generally favours following traditional lines. In many ways I felt inhibited, as I wished at the very least to incorporate some of the fresh techniques that I had encountered on my travels, or failing that introduce some ideas of my own, though we did enact some changes as larger tractors and combines replaced smaller models. The old David Brown crawlers and their towed ploughs were phased out, and replaced with tractor mounted 3 and then 4 furrow ploughs.

If we wished to find full employment for our large labour force totalling 11 men including John and me in 1970 we realised that we had to introduce more labour intensive enterprises. Through a long standing friendship with Graham and Marion Shaw from Wainfleet that started when we met through the YFC movement in 1960 and still continues to this today, we started to grow 20 acres of Dutch winter cabbage on contract to his uncle Cyril of Shaw Bros who were produce merchants at Friskney. When I saw their production of cabbage I thought that this was a crop that we could grow successfully as our land was clear of the dreaded club root virus, and at a stroke would provide additional employment for our men. So it was that we started to grow some of the labour intensive crops that were more commonly grown in the south of the county. In addition to growing cabbage we decided to grow ten acres of Brussel sprouts for freezing. Unfortunately the freezing company had contracted for more sprouts than they had the capacity to process through their factory. So it wasn't too successful. We also tried growing sugar beet, which although it paid quite well with a contractor doing the actual lifting, it was something of a nightmare carting the beet off our wet fields in November. It resulted in enormous ruts causing serious damage to the soil structure for following crops.

Perhaps it had something to do with the optimism and impatience of youth that I wished to be paddling my own canoe and learn by my own mistakes. One of the fundamental lessons that I learned whilst meeting and talking to so many people on my journeys, was that it was most unlikely that a person would make any headway in business unless they were prepared to be receptive to new ideas and take risks. I was mindful that I was a minority shareholder in a "closed" company were my proportion of the farms shares had little market value. No one was realistically going to pay much for shares that were untraded, unless they had a prospect of buying many more in order that they could hold over 50%, which was most unlikely to occur. Even with the addition of my father's shareholding it was impossible to split the company without the compliance of both sides of the family.

A principle advantage of size however, meant that John was able to follow his father specializing in the arable side of the farm, whist I in turn followed my father dealing with the livestock side. I gradually took over livestock marketing seeking out and selling our Lincoln Red bulls and females to many parts of the country. It proved impossible to sell all of the cattle as pedigrees because there was insufficient demand for all the pedigree Lincoln Reds that we were producing. Inevitably a significant proportion of the herd were sold as commercial fat stock. In my father's day many of the cattle were sold on a regular basis through Louth cattle market, with Frank Mawer a quality butcher trading in Louth's Mercer Row, being a regular buyer of Cockerington cattle. When Mr Mawer retired we started to sell our finished cattle on a dead weight basis with animals going to Anglia Quality Meat a farmer's co operative based in

Lincolnshire Standard press cutting.

149

Royston in Hertfordshire. I became a director of that company attending their board meetings at Royston along with Mr Norman Borill of South Cockrington Grange, a fellow director.

At a time when there was a great deal of restructuring and specialization occurring on British farms, we seemed to be reluctant to accept the radical changes that were a necessary requirement to meet the new challenges that lay ahead. As other farms reduced their labour force by specialization, we retained all our workers by introducing new labour intensive crops to provide employment for them all whilst still continuing with many of the enterprises that we had had for many years.

In 1972 we decided to diversify further into horticultural type crops by growing an acre of daffodils for both cut flowers and bulb production. This was a crop that had traditionally been grown on the easily worked, silt soils around Spalding in south Lincolnshire. Mr. Peter Lubbe from Haarlem in northern Holland was a very keen and enthusiastic Dutch grower and salesman. For many years he had very successfully traded bulbs in the Spalding area. When he ventured north onto the heavier soils in the Louth area of North Lincolnshire he was able to put up a sound argument for growing daffodil bulbs on the recently ploughed up, fibre rich grassland soils that would be eel worm free (a major pest of daffodil bulbs) making it ideal land for bulb production. We in common with a few other local farmers saw that there could be an economic return in growing daffodil bulbs. We decided to purchase five tons of yellow trumpeted Carlton daffodils at £280 per ton which we planted in one acre of particularly easy working soil that had been ploughed out of permanent grassland some ten years earlier. We lifted the bulbs in early July every second year using an old single row potato lifter that exposed the white fibrous roots to the air in order that they could wither and dry. We then handpicked them into 1 ton boxes that were moved by a forklift truck, to the yard where soil and debris was riddled off on a special bulb grader. The dry clumps of bulbs could then be broken up and graded for size with the very small and the very large bulbs being retained for replanting again as seed. The midsized bulbs were finally weighed off according to size into 56lb nets for sale.

The superior quality of our disease free, prolific flowering bulbs found a ready market for export back to Holland for forcing as cut flowers, resulting in the one acre of bulbs quickly expanding to sixteen acres and eight different varieties.

From the second year my wife Pat organised a team of up to 15 local ladies who came suitably clad in waterproof trousers, coats and gloves as a defence against the cold and wet that seemed to characterise the difficult working conditions in the early spring to pick the flowers. Once the flower stems were about 10 inches long but still in tight bud, looking rather like green pencils they were picked and bunched in tens with an elastic band, then up to 80 bunches were packed in a cardboard flower box. During the peak picking period they would pick up to eighty boxes a day. These cut flowers went to a wide variety of destinations, ranging from local florists, to the wholesale market in Hull, and in later years to Spalding for export in chilled containers to the Continent and even North America.

Picking the dry bulbs from the fields in July necessitated employing some of the local women who had helped Pat earlier in the year to pick flowers. They were supplemented by older school children after they broke up for the summer holidays. Unfortunately this casual labour was very unreliable as we were never quite sure how many, if any would turn up to work. We paid them daily on the quantity that they picked, resulting in many of them wanting to go and spend their money as soon as they had earned a few pounds. Organising a regular picking labour force became a nightmare as there were constant complaints of the weather being either, "too hot" or "too cold", or it was "too windy", or the ground was "too dusty" or "too hard". This led us to take the decision to phase out the enterprise in 1990, (7 years after we split the farm when needed to make drastic savings in labour because by then there were only three of us working on the farm). More about splitting the farm later.

In 1970 we decided to start a self pick, Raspberry enterprise, growing two acres of canes. Four parallel wires were attached to twenty five rows of posts that had been cut from Elm trees recently killed by Dutch elm disease in the bottom plantations. I was able to obtain a sufficient quantity of a vigorous Raspberry variety called 'Glen Clova' from one of my Scottish bull contacts on one of my frequent bull deliveries to Scotland. The self pick operation started production in 1972 when an old caravan was purchased which acted as the base for selling. The self pick soft fruit enterprise was only partially successful as there were several drawbacks paramount of which was that it tied one person – usually Pat - to the selling caravan for the duration of the picking season. In spite of growing an amazing quantity of excellent fruit we were unable to attract sufficient customers when the fruit was at its best resulting in much of the crop being wasted.

Both of these enterprises were very labour intensive which made them difficult to justify with the dramatic reduction in labour that came about by the reorganisation of the farm in 1982. Many of our farm enterprises have necessitated meeting members of the public either to pick fruit, bulbs and flowers or to look at the breeding cattle, all of which involved varying degrees of public relations diplomacy.

Early in 1982 it became apparent that the interests of John and I would be best served if the company was demerged to form two new independent companies. The restructuring revolution that had swept through so many British farms during the 1970s finally caught up with us allowing the two families' to remodel their farms in preparation for leaner times ahead. The inevitable outcome was that we reluctantly had to make almost half of our employees redundant in order that the businesses could remain viable.

CHAPTER 14
A New Era

My farming life took a major change on January 1st 1983 when rather like hearing the firing of a starter's gun I commenced farming in my own right, which in many ways placed me in a similar position to the one that my grandfather found himself in 100 years earlier when he started to farm independently. During the previous year John and I had decided that in view of planning a future for the next generation that it was now an appropriate time to demerge the original farming company into two totally separate enterprises. Just as a pendulum that has reached the end of its swing in one direction the speed of change was dramatic. Demerging the business into two separate entities's caused the pendulum to sharply reverse its direction of travel, providing in its wake sweeping changes in working practices.

The major restructuring exercise that followed in order that the farm could remain viable to face the challenging times that lay ahead, made it inevitable that several of the existing labour force who had worked for us for a number of years would regrettably have to be made redundant. For at least the previous ten years when other local farms were shedding much of their labour, we found employment for at least a third more men than was strictly necessary for a farm of our size, as was abundantly clear when our two new separate farms managed all the work by employing two men each.

At the age of 46 it enabled me, to put some of my ideas into practice and expand on some of the projects that we had started to introduce with the old company in recent years. Because of the revenues rules relating to demerging companies and majority shareholdings and unforseen by our solicitors and accountants from Birmingham who specialised in company law I was saddled with a £50,000 tax demand in addition to expenditure of more than £100,000 that was necessary for the purchase of essential farm machinery, which meant that I was burdened with a hefty overdraft.

The phrase, "that it's in the blood", must have been invented with someone like my son Alistair in mind because he had never wanted to do anything else other than farm. Why else would want to want to work all hours often in very unpleasant climatic conditions, always at the mercy of the weather and politicians manipulating prices? It's probably the only industry that purchases all of its inputs retail and sells everything wholesale? However my answer to complaining farmers is that we are all volunteers. Of course there are countless benefits that I for one would be reluctant to sacrifice, such as the thrill of seeing the birth of a healthy pedigree calf and watching its development over the next couple of years, leading to the time when in the case of a bull calf it's sold to become someones new stock bull in a different part of the country. A female calf will either be retained in the herd for the next 10 years or form part of an entirely new pedigree herd somewhere else.

There's something immensely satisfying about walking through a covered yard of in calf cows, on a cold winters night. They are unconcerned with my presence as they continue to contentedly chew their cud whilst laying dry and warm, inside a building, on a bed of clean straw. It's also hard to beat that feeling of euphoria on a sunny May morning when new life and fresh optimism is busting throughout the countryside. Then a few weeks later to enjoy the evocative smell of new mown hay, all

A group of cows and calves in our Charolais herd.

of which more than makes up for the long hours at harvest time and the mud and cold of the winter months.

My share of cattle following the demerger comprised a mixture of Lincoln Red and Charolais, along with several cross bred calves. Faced with the decision to maximise income from the pedigree herd, I took a similar route to the one employed by my grandfather. This was to sell the less profitable Lincoln Red and Angus cross cattle in order that I could specialize on an all white Pedigree Charolais herd. I reckoned the measure would add an enhanced pedigree value to the herd enabling me to sell the sought after pedigree Charolais breeding stock to farmers all over the U K. Within three years I had sold all the Lincoln Red and crossbred animals, retaining all white cattle in order to rapidly build up an all pedigree Charolais herd. Mr J T Henwood who was the Limousin breed secretary invited me to give a paper on polling to their society and other interested pedigree breed society members at the Royal Show ground in April 1985. This well attended event was extremely successful contributing greatly to recognition of the Cockerington herd as a leading Charolais herd. The meeting was important for another significant reason as it introduced me to a group of Charolais breeders who had imported a poll Charolais bull from Canada and had formed a new society entitled The Poll Charolais Cattle Society of Great Britain. (The British Charolais Cattle Society at that time were disinclined to register polls within their herd book.) The new Poll Society invited me to join them which I was happy to do, when Poll Charolais that we had been breeding at Cockerington formed a significant proportion of their first herd book. The new society flourished under the secretaryship of Len Hayton, a solicitor with his offices in Windermere, and an enthusiastic council comprising members from all over the country. I was appointed to their council and over the next 4 years spent many enjoyable days accompanied by Robert Needham who also joined the council, attending meetings at a hotel just outside Windermere. Development of the herd made rapid progress during the next three years with the sale of Cockerington Baron to The Milk Marketing Board in January 1988 for £6000 and a little later in the year we sold Cockerington Brookside also for £6000 to be exported to South Africa.

Now that the farm had a small staff I needed to operate high quality, reliable, farm equipment that for the most part would be covered by a dealers warranty. I wanted to establish a policy of changing machinery on a very regular basis and thus eliminate costly repairs. Perhaps of even

Marshall Threshing Set from a painting by and courtesy of Robin Wheeldon

Note the Field Marshall tractors manufactured in Gainsborough and also the winding barrow, near the grain man in the foreground, which was used to raise sacks of grain to shoulder height in order that they could be carried.

Our Massey Ferguson Combine harvesting wheat and discharging grain into an 18 ton trailor.

greater importance I wanted to eliminate the frustration of a machine breaking down at a critical time. The tractors were swiftly changed to new Fiats with a three year warranty supplied by The Burgess group based in Northgate Louth. We received excellent support from them until the branch closed in 1986, when the site was sold to make way for the new Co-Op supermarket. Machinery business was then transferred to Peacock & Binnington when the tractor fleet was changed to Massey Ferguson and we adopted a policy of replacing our combine and tractors with new machines every three years.

My first years cropping in 1983 comprised of 154 acres of winter wheat, 104 acres of winter barley, and 54 acres of oilseed rape plus 15 acres of daffodils and 2 acres of self pick raspberries, making a grand total of 329 arable acres.

Our bulb enterprise which is also mentioned elsewhere was quite profitable bringing in a good source of revenue during a period of heavy investment on the farm but suffered from unreliable casual labour at critical times, so was gradually phased out.

As the children grew older they left their Primary School and moved on to secondary school at Monks Dyke and King Edwards, when in order that I could follow their education more closely I joined the respective governing bodies of both schools, eventually becoming chairman in due course. In 1981 my public work continued when I was honoured to be appointed a magistrate that led to me attending court on more than 30 occasions each year in the company of 11, other colleagues on the Louth bench, sitting at the courthouse near the Bede Houses in Eastgate.

I found the work stimulating, as it gave me an opportunity to see firsthand another side of society that hither to had only come through selectively edited newspaper reports of court cases. I hoped that my views contributed to the balance of the bench offering a sense of practicality into our decisions. Regrettably I had to resign in 1989 when I found that the commitment was too onerous, as it was having a serious effect on my availability to carry out seasonal work on the farm that required the full labour force of three to take advantage of changing weather conditions.

Alistair joined me on the farm in 1984, having like me, a lifelong unswerving ambition to make a career in agriculture. Over the course of the next two years the two men who joined us in 1983 moved on to other farms in North Lincolnshire, so that when Alistair and I discussed the situation we thought that we could farm our acreage effectively ourselves with the addition of part time help during peak periods. The part time man that we employed during the summer of 1985 proved to be unsatisfactory as his inflexibility was at complete odds with the new ideas that we wished to introduce so we decided to employ Adrian Clark, a 15 year old lad who had just left school, on a youth scheme. He responded to the challenge as we have always kept him informed of our plans for the farms development. From the earliest time when he attended day release classes at Louth Agriculture College we have encouraged him to learn new skills and take any appropriate exams, resulting in him still being on the farm over 25 years later. One of the farms redundant cottages was sold in 1988 to fund part of the cost of a new, drive on, floor grain store. This gave us much greater flexibility in drying crops such as Oil Seed Rape before the seed was transferred into one of our 6 x 150 ton round grain silos.

By the end of 1988 we were totally in control of all the land that we were then farming in spite of the fact that the horticultural enterprises were very time consuming and could not achieve their true potential. The Raspberries' had a further complication as they were becoming infested with nettles and thistles that were almost impossible to successfully eradicate.

The decision was taken to terminate the enterprise and reseed the area with grass so that it could be reunited with the rest of the grass field. We also decided to phase out the daffodil bulbs for the reasons mentioned previously which we accomplished in 1990, when the last 4 tons of very tiny bulbs were replanted at the southern end of a field near the home farmyard. In the early spring of 1992 we planted a total of 5 acres of seedling, one year old, broadleaved trees comprising a mixture of Oak, Beech, Sycamore, Sweet Chestnut and Field Maple, to create several new woods in various parts of the farm. Two acres were planted over the daffodil rows with further areas planted within the sweeping curves of the beck to replace the trees that had been lost to Dutch Elm disease in the 1960s. The trees grew remarkably quickly so that by 2008 we were able to carry out a major thinning process when many of them had grown to be more than 30 feet tall.

At the end of October 1988, on a cold, wet afternoon, Pat and I were on our way to attend an art exhibition at Weston Longville near Norwich,

Dead heading and show preparation are Pat Needham's contribution to her husband Ralph's success in the challenging field of orchid propagation.

A talent with orchids...

A love of the exotic and good husbandry have helped Ralph Needham turn a hobby into a sideline and changed the view from the farm kitchen sink. Judy Steele reports

FOUR years ago Ralph Needham of South Cockerington, Lincs, had four orchids. Now he has a wholesale business with about 2000 plants and 25,000 pleione (hardy orchid) bulbs and fits their care around his 227ha (560-acre) farm.

"The buzz with orchid growing is in trying to grow at 56 north something that was designed to grow within 20 of the Equator," he says.

Ralph is well known among cattle breeding circles for the polled Charolais strain he has spent many years producing. He sees his orchid growing as a natural continuation of his farming enterprise. The challenge of producing top pedigree cattle, and the husbandry involved, apply just as well to growing orchids, he says.

The enterprise fits in well with the farm. The plants are watered every 10 days or so in winter and every four in the heat of the summer. Even at the peak of

harvest Ralph can water every plant in half an hour. The main work comes in early November and February when it's quiet on the farm.

Although his wife Pat does not help with the day-to-day care of the plants, except for removing dead leaves and heads, her skills are needed when it's time to get ready for a show. It's painstaking work, as every leaf has to be carefully washed and flowering spikes must be meticulously tied to make a pleasing display.

Ralph has always been interested in gardening but likes to grow things that are slightly exotic. He began growing orchids almost by chance when he stumbled upon an orchid nursery.

Before he started growing in earnest Ralph did some serious research. He read as many books as he could find and visited a lot of nurseries, including the Eric Young Foundation in Jersey. The four plants he started with increased to 1000 in six months and he had to build a greenhouse attached to the house to put them in. The heat-loving moth orchids live there now and give Pat an exotic view as she does the washing up.

Ralph had always considered the commercial possibilities of the venture — he had seen a gap in the market. "The first nursery

Phalaenopsis (moth orchid).

Cymbidium Baltic Honey.

I went to see was fine for specialists but you would be buying a bunch of green leaves." The big four- to five-year-old plants in flower were not for sale. "I thought there was a market for people who wanted to buy plants in flower. I would consider selling every plant I have." A small specimen in flower, suitable for the home, would cost from £11 to £15 but rare and prized examples will cost much more.

Soon Ralph needed more space and built a large greenhouse close to the back of his home. He now has three zones of heat to suit the different types of orchid. The lean-to greenhouse where the phalaenopsis are grown is kept at 18C (64F); the intermediate zone, which houses the majority of the plants, is kept at 14C (56F); and there is a cool zone which holds the pleiones at a minimum of 5C (42F). The intermediate house also has slightly different zones which mimic the climatic conditions preferred by the plants, from the cloud layers of the Andes where the miltonopsis grow, to the forest floor, the habitat of the cattleyas.

Although he won a cup last year for the best plant in show when exhibiting with the East Midlands Orchid Society at Harrogate against eight other clubs,

continued over ▶

Farmers Weekly 26 February 1993

Farmlife 1

Extract of Farmers Weekly article 26 February 1993.

Our award winning Catlea plant.

when we spotted a yellow AA directional sign on the side of the A17 near Kings Lynn, pointing down a side road, for an display described as "Orchid World". Curious as to the nature of the attraction we decided that time permitting on our return we would drive down and see what it was all about. We were both totally unprepared for the spectacular array of vibrant colours from the many types of orchid plants that greeted us when we stepped inside a large glasshouse. In an instant we were transported from a dark winters afternoon in Lincolnshire, to a tropical paradise with a brilliantly lit display of exotic flowers in bloom. In spite of being a lifelong keen gardener with a bent for growing unusual plants generally from much warmer climes, the sum total of my knowledge of orchids could be summarised in three words, exotic, expensive, difficult. Ted Lloyd the owner of Orchid World had moved to North Norfolk from the London area following a career in computer technology in order that he could indulge his passion for growing orchids. He was sufficiently enthralled with them that he passed some of that enthusiasm on to me that afternoon. This resulted in me purchasing 8 orchid plants. With a sensible observation from Pat of *"where do you think you are going to grow them, we haven't got the right conditions?"*, ringing in my ears I carefully carried the potted plants back to the car. Always ready for a challenge I assured her that armed with the book that I had just purchased, entitled "Orchids For All", I was confident that I would be able to successfully grow orchids. Depositing the black plant pots containing their assortment of green leaved plants some of which were devoid of even the hint of a flower bud on a windowsill, I immersed myself in the pages of the book and learned something of the enormous complexity of the genre. I discovered that the twenty five thousand species of orchids could be found pretty well all over the world, ranging from tiny Alpine orchids growing in the very cool conditions of the high latitudes to the exotic flowers of orchids growing in the shadowy depths of a tropical rain forest.

All orchids are epiphytes which mean that they grow attached to rocks or the bark on trees extracting moisture from rain or in the case of tropical orchids from areas of high humidity, in complete contrast to a parasitic plant such as mistletoe that draws feed from its host. Referring to my bible like book I read about the colourful cymbidiums that flowered from amidst reed like leaves. They originated from the foothills of the Himalayas, and could be found growing naturally in an arc stretching down into South East Asia. I gathered that they would send up flowering spikes from their pseudo bulbs as the winter progressed and come into bloom from February to April. Two of the other plants were much more compact with swollen stems and quite thick fleshy leaves that I discovered were called Catleyas originating from the rain forests of central and South America. The final two plants were compact plants called Phalenopsis with very broad fleshy leaves whose natural habitat was one of deep shade under the tree canopy of South East Asian rain forests.

At a time when there was a dearth of farmland coming on to the market and we were ready to expand our farm acreage, I considered that there were commercial possibilities of growing orchids as a means of diversification. Rising to the challenge of growing orchids I went down to Mr Lloyds Orchid World a fortnight later and purchased a further selection of plants, along with two bags of water repellent and water absorbent rock wool fibre that Mr Lloyd had developed as a growing medium in which to support the plants. Realising that I would now require an orchid greenhouse I employed Bruce Stapleton a joiner friend

Conscience Hill

from Saltfleetby to build a lean to conservatory on the eastern side of our house, ensuring that it was built to a sufficiently high standard in order that it would add value to the house in the event of the sale of the property in the future.

On my next visit to Norfolk in January 1989 Mr Lloyd showed me a small alpine like orchid called Pleione whose pseudo bulbs meant that they had vague similarities to growing daffodil bulbs. Although Pleiones like daffodils flower from a dormant bulb in the spring, there the similarities ended because Pleiones needed to be grown in 6 inch deep trays of a peat based compost and placed in a cool greenhouse. The bulbs were in fact a pseudo bulb much more akin to a crocus than a daffodil. Unlike daffodil bulbs that were sold by weight between July and October when the bulbs were dormant, we discovered that Pleione bulbs because of their much greater value were priced individually, with a higher value attached to the larger bulbs. They were usually marketed in their dormant state following lifting between November and February. However they had a major advantage over daffodils as they could also be sold as a pot plant in the spring for either Mothers Day or Easter. It was a simple task to lift the growing bulbs with the flowers in tight bud from the trays of peat and pot them off into plant pots.

As our daffodil enterprise had virtually finished by this time, I thought that growing Pleiones could be a rewarding enterprise, as we could carry out all the work ourselves inside a building during the early winter at a slack time in the farming year, and further more I would be dealing in a high value product aimed at the impulse buying market. I located a specialist Pleione grower near Spalding and managed to purchase 5,000 bulbs from him followed by a quantity of black trays to grow them in from a dispersal sale of horticultural sundries near Boston. By March 1st 1989 I had planted them all in a mixture of peat and Perlite at the rate of 50 bulbs to the box and placed them on the floor of my old wooden Dutch light type greenhouse that I had bought second hand many years previously and was now situated at the bottom of the garden. During that first growing season I realised that I didn't have ideal growing conditions for growing Pleiones. My low roofed greenhouse became too hot during the sunniest part of the day, resulting in some scorching to the leaves, so I decided that for the following year I would purchase a poly tunnel as it would be much easier to regulate the temperature and air flow because I could open either end to create a cooling draught. With the poly tunnel

162

erected at the end of the garden, for the following season I placed the Pleiones at one end and grew the rest of my vegetable crops in the remaining area, achieving fantastic results in the exceptionally favourable growing conditions.

The Pleiones grew well producing a sea of delicate mauve flowers during April that gave way to a forest of ten inch high strap like emerald green leaves as spring gave way to summer. Then as the days shortened and the autumn nights drew in the leaves turned various shades of fawn as the plants senesced and entered their period of dormancy. In early November we lifted the bulbs from their boxes of peat based material and snipped off the roots and dead foliage discovering that some of the bulbs had been replaced by much larger ones, whilst others had multiplied into several smaller ones.

By 1990 it became apparent that the conservatory was not suitable for my other orchid plants. It was too low and quickly got too hot, so I decided to indulge in a new green house equipped with automatic vents, thermostatic heating and special reflective shading. The greenhouse was erected in August 1990 enabling me to transfer my burgeoning collection of Cymbidiums, Cattleyas and other species to a much better regulated atmosphere.

Pat and I joined the East Midlands Orchid Society and regularly attended their monthly meetings at Stoke Rochford Hall near Grantham, when an eminent orchid grower would speak on various topics relating to growing orchids. We entered some of our flowering plants in the monthly competitions learning how to correctly present them and more importantly compete against growers of many years standing. The society exhibited a display at orchid shows in different parts of the country when the members supplied the flowering plants which were judged and prize rosettes awarded for different classifications. A Catleya with half a dozen green leaves that had formed a part of my very first purchase from Orchid World flowered for the first time the following October and then at about the same time each subsequent year with an ever increasing multitude of pale yellow flowers surrounding a rich magenta trumpet. The plant began to win awards in 1991 and by 1992 it was obvious that it was enjoying our conditions as it continued to grow in size, leading Pat and I to have high hopes for the British National Orchid Show, as its rotation around the country brought it to Lincoln in November 1993.

Although the plant was full of buds by the end of October we felt that it would not be at its best for another three weeks so consequently did not have very high expectations of success. As we had a prior engagement. on the first day of the show we arrived to collect our plants on the second day at the conclusion of the show. We were greeted by a fellow society member in the car park "saying have you brought a trailer for your awards". It transpired that in addition to awards for some of our other plants the Cattleya had won its class and then gone on to win the supreme champion in the show with Pat and I receiving an enormous silver and gold punch bowl.

Ted Lloyd's Orchid World business collapsed in January 1992 when I went down to Terrington for the final time to see a forlorn figure with his orchid dream shattered. I believe that his business had a serious flaw. I discovered that he was renting his glasshouses, and had invested too heavily in infrastructure. It might have worked in the home county's, but not on the sparsley populated area near Kings Lynn. As his heating had been turned off I rescued a few plants and brought them home, but they did not thrive as they had been severely chilled with most of them dying over the course of the next few weeks. Regrettably most of our orchids had to be sold off during the winter of 1994/95 as a result of us expanding the farm by purchasing an additional 150 acres and moving to Ivy House Farm in Grimoldby.

As the house was grade two listed we were refused planning permission to move the greenhouse and poly tunnel for re-erection near the house or farmyard. As a result we were left with no alternative other than to sell them and dispose of most of our orchids. One of the biggest disappointments was the disposal of the Pleione stock as numbers were beginning to increase quite rapidly as I refined my growing technique.

CHAPTER 15
It's all happening

The four years from 1989 to 1993 were in many ways quite frustrating as we wanted to expand our farmed area, but unfortunately there was a complete dearth of local land coming on to the market, which was one of the reasons that Orchid growing offered the possibility of diversification whilst fulfilling my passion for growing 'something exotic'. I was enough of a realist to know that for the flowering plant market to be economically successful in this rural backwater of the country in North Lincolnshire we could never generate sufficient customers, but it had been an extremely enjoyable enterprise whilst it lasted.

However the few small land purchases that we made acted rather like a dress rehearsal to several major changes in the farms composition that commenced in 1994, and ran until 2002. This resulted in the area that we farmed almost trebling. In June 1990 we purchased a 4.5 acre field up Stewton Lane from Frank Nicholson for £10,000, (£2222 per acre) plus £1300 (£290 per acre) for the growing crop of wheat. Both prices were considerably higher than the current market value but we felt it was a price worth paying as our land surrounded this relatively small field. We then decided to market a small area of land in South View Lane within the village for four building plots that was proving very difficult to farm as it was surrounded at either end of the plots by houses. Our next purchase occurred in August 1991 when two small farmers with land to sell responded to our advert in the local paper when we sought offers from people with land to sell. The first man offered us 33.5 acres, made up of 6 quite small fields. When Alistair and I walked over the land we discovered that the fields were not only divided by a complex arrangement of internal ditches, but pretty well all the land was heavily infested with thistles, docks and nettles along with outcrops of discarded poly baler twine.

In spite of the considerable expense that would be necessary to rectify years of neglect we didn't quibble with the sellers asking price. We needed to spread our investment in new machinery over more acres at a time when there was little or no local land coming on to the market. The other sellers land comprised a further 16 acres in two separate fields of which the first 6 acre field was exceptionally wet. This was no doubt the reason that 70 or more years earlier the field had been rigged up with nets to catch lapwings or plovers as they are more commonly known locally, when the birds were a highly valued delicacy.

However all traces of the nets had long since disappeared with the wet field now growing a rather poor looking crop of grass to make into hay. It did have the advantage of abutting the other owners six small fields, and could relatively easily be amalgamated into them, by filling in the adjoining ditch, and under draining it along with the other land. By early October we had the land drained, ploughed and drilled with winter wheat. The remaining 10 acre field had a roadside frontage situated a short distance away which we also under drained.

I record in my diary for 1991 that the first rain for two months fell over the last weekend in September when we received over 50 mm of rain, this enabled us to complete drilling 413 acres of crops on October 16th.

On March 6th 1992 we successfully tendered for 25.5 acres of grassland from Mr Harold West of Pickhill in Grimoldby. It comprised several fields divided by enormous hawthorn and blackthorn hedges standing as much as 6 to 8 meter high, and spreading sideways for a similar distance, with outcrops of briars spreading even further into the fields and choking the grass. We cleared the central area whilst leaving the overgrown perimeter hedges largely intact as it was a wonderful source of wild life on the hedge-less marsh landscape.

In May 1994 we became quite excited when we spotted an advertisement in the Farmers Weekly from Bidwells of Cambridge who were offering the 314 acre Red Leas Farm in North Cockerington for sale by private treaty. This was one of those rare events in farming when an almost next door farm comes on to the market. It presented us with a fantastic opportunity to make a major expansion, especially as the farm was only a couple of miles away from the South Cockerington home farm.

Although the farm had a rather poor reputation for being very wet with a severe drainage problem on the heavy clay soils, we thought it could be made into a very productive unit given careful management. The key was to satisfactorily evacuate water from the farm to prevent extensive flooding that used to happen on a quite regular basis following heavy rain. Our hopes were dashed when we were informed that it had been sold prior to the advertisement appearing in the Farmers Weekly and had been purchased by Anglian Water. We wrote to Anglian Water including testimonials from a wide spectrum of professional and trades people who dealt with us, suggesting that they might consider an old family business such as ours as suitable tenants to care for their new farm, but this unfortunately was to no avail, as Anglian Water declared that they would continue for the time being with the existing tenants.

So it was that with even keener anticipation we tendered for Messrs Cheffings 170 acre Grimoldby Farm in August 1994 when the brothers decided to retire from farming. On this occasion our tender was successful. That allowed us, under the scrutiny of the conservation officer, to carry out a restoration programme on the grade 2 Ivy House where Pat and I would move the following January. Electric wiring required renewal, and a completely new plumbing and heating system was installed, in addition to renewing much of the plaster including many of the ceilings.

In order to partially fund the purchase we decided to sell 4 of our smaller more distant fields along with our home in South Cockerington,

Three months later in November 1994 whilst in the midst of carrying out our alterations to Ivy House, we received a call, completely out of the blue from Mr Hugo Bolus. He was responsible for Anglian Water's property, and wished to discuss the possibility of us renting Red Leas Farm and running it as a model farm with green credentials. We readily acceded to their request adding that as one of the very first participants of the recently introduced farm business tenancies, we needed security of tenure for at least 20 years in order that we could address some of the farms problems.

The farm had a notorious reputation for being very wet as it was low lying and consequently frequently flooded. It was also heavily infested with black grass and had a major compaction problem. This was largely caused by the previous tenants attempts to construct seed beds by working the soil before it was in a satisfactory working condition. Drainage had always been a concern on the farm, as the only method of evacuating water from the low lying land was via a flap valve that discharged into the South Drain (a highland water carrier that conveyed water from the the eastern side of the wolds). In spite of the fact that the farm was within the LMDB area and consequently paid drainage rates, there was no method of getting the water into the LMDB's pumped system. In an endeavour to avoid the frequent flooding that occurred when the South Drain was full of water, Mr Symington who farmed Red Leas in the 1950s installed a small diesel pump to lift water out of the farm ditches into the South Drain. By the time that our association with Red Leas commenced, the pump had long since ceased working, if indeed it ever did work effectively due to its very limited capacity. Regrettably due to lack of maintenance by the Environmental Agency the South Drain had become heavily silted making it increasingly difficult for water to be evacuated from the farm. On several occasions from the year 2000 onwards there was severe flooding on the farm when up to 70 acres lay under water for several days on end.

Flooding at Red Leas following heavy rain January 2000. Note the old pump house in the centre left of the photograph

Amalgamating Red Leas and Ivy House Farm into the existing farm worked surprisingly well, considering that we continued to do all the work with the three of us namely, Alistair, Adrian and myself. Commencing in 1995 we started to invest in much larger equipment to cope with the additional acreage that included an additional big tractor along with new grass harvesting machinery, plough, drill and power harrows. We hired a contractor, who cleared the internal ditches of years of accumulated mud and decaying vegetation, in an attempt to evacuate water quicker. In spite

The result of a moderate rain in February 2002. The old pump house can be seen in the top left of the picture.

of all our efforts to improve the farms drainage, the fundamental problem lay in the Environment Agency's dereliction of duty in not properly maintaining their watercourses. However a permanent solution to the problem was carried out by Lindsey Marsh Drainage Board, in December 2005 when a 300 mm siphon was thrust under the bed of the South Drain enabling the water to enter their pumped system, after which the water table in the internal ditches dropped by more than three feet.

If Britain is serious about having food security for the nation, then we neglect drainage at our peril, as it's impossible to grow crops on land that does not have satisfactory drainage.

In 1988 the British Charolais Cattle Society appointed Mr David Benson as their new secretary who helped facilitate the merger of both charolais societies during 1989 leading to full amalgamation on January 1st 1990. I was invited to join the new combined council as a previous member of the poll Charolais society, leading to my appointment as national chairman of The British Charolais Cattle Society in 1995/96. I served at various terms on the council until 2010, first as council member representing the East Midlands then as the first National council member. During my year as Chairman news broke on March 20th 1996, that there was a strong

Thrust boring in progress to go under the bed of the South Drain.

Looking towards the Old Pump House. Note: The South Drain beyond the tree.

Lindsey Marsh's finished job along with the new water level in the ditch

possibility of BSE in cattle being passed on to humans in the human form of CYD. This announcement had a devastating effect right across the farming industry leading to a spiralling reduction in farm gate prices that would depress the industry for the next 11 years. Under the new regulations any animal over thirty months of age had to be incinerated, at enormous cost to the country. Alarmist propaganda was constantly being aired by the media and recycled by people who claimed to be experts, revelling in their new found claim to fame, suggesting that we were likely to lose a generation of young people. Whilst there have certainly been cases of CJD, which must have been devastating to the families of the people concerned, the numbers have been very small compared to the projected figures. Furthermore, a definitive link has still not been established between cattle and humans, though thankfully the number of cattle cases is now down to minimal levels in 2011.

Alistair and I, as tenants of Anglian Water, attended monthly meetings at Red Leas Farm, when the various departments of Anglian Water reported on their respective projects to turn the farm into a demonstration unit that was designed to promote the use of what was termed 'bio degradables'. A butyl, lined lagoon, with embanked earth walls, was erected to hold partially treated, sewage sludge for injecting under the cultivated soil, following ploughing after each harvest. In addition, independently regulated trials were carried out by ADAS using many types of treated sludge in order to evaluate the fertiliser value of different products linked to a range of application rates. Other departments replanted hedges and created new woodland areas under the general heading of conservation. Another department dealt with public relations and embarked on a project that would turn the farmhouse into an educational training centre. Their objective was to turn the farm into a model farm of excellence with ourselves farming the land in a sympathetic manner.

It's quite possible that their policy of carrying out a fully transparent operation with absolutely nothing to hide, worked to Anglian Water's disadvantage. It alerted a near neighbour to health disasters that might occur as a result of incorporating processed sewage into agricultural land. The technique of using untreated raw sewage at vastly greater concentrations has been employed for hundreds of years in domestic gardens as the principle method of fertilizing the ground, with no ill effects to people who ate the garden produce. The neighbour soon gained local notoriety by advancing all manner of potential disaster type scenarios. Almost overnight he promoted himself as an expert in micro biology at a time when the hysteria surrounding BSE was spreading its catalogue of alarmist propaganda. Even experts found it impossible to argue with 100% certainty that any event however remote could never occur, so it became very easy for the doom mongers to make all manner of wild suggestions in the full knowledge that their prognosis could never be fully denied.

As compulsory set aside became a farming feature we ceased to crop the more difficult heavy clay soils with the flood prone fields of Red Leas providing a major portion of the farms obligatory set-aside. In spite of the severe downturn in prices with wheat halving in value between 1984 and 1997 we continued to change all of our machinery every three years ensuring that the new models were significantly better than those that they replaced.

On February 23rd 2001 a major Foot and Mouth outbreak occurred in the UK that effectively destroyed all pedigree cattle trade for over a year, resulting in most of our 2001 breeding bulls being sold at a heavily discounted price for beef. My diary records 19 breeding bulls being sent to ABP at York and sold at a price of less than one fifth of their breeding value as they were considered too heavy for the normal fat stock trade.

Even though the nearest case of foot and mouth disease was more than 100 miles away it had a devastating effect on pedigree livestock sales for more than a year, as cattle movements other than for slaughter were prohibited. The dramatic reduction in pedigree sales had severe ramifications throughout the livestock industry with consequential big drops in income, including our own.

In early 2001 Anglian Water had a change of policy and decided to sell the 314 acres Red Leas Farm, allowing us as sitting tenants to have the first chance to purchase it at a full open market value. In order to finance the purchase we decided to sell our renovated Ivy House where we had lived since 1995 along with the farmyard and the two grass fields that surrounded the property, and build a property attached to the western end of my mother's bungalow at Hall Farm, South Cockerington. Basic plans were drawn up over the space of two weeks in order that a planning application could be lodged by early March in order for it to be considered at the April 5th planning meeting. The local planning officer was decidedly unhelpful as he endeavoured to present every obstacle that he could possibly think of to block the application. It was absolutely vital to the future viability of the farm that we did our upmost to retain Red Leas farm as it then accounted for almost a third of our acreage. Anglian Water had given us an undertaking only 6 years earlier that we would be able to rent the farm from them for the next 20 years, with the result that we had invested a considerable sum of money into the farm by way of draining and other cultivation practices to improve soil structure, along with a costly programme to rid the farm of black grass and wild oats. We had purchased bigger and better machines in the confident knowledge that we could justify the additional expense by spreading the cost over a greater acreage.

But, irrespective of any issues regarding raising the necessary finance to purchase Red Leas farm, there were important welfare issue at stake that would justify my movement to Hall Farm in any case. By living adjacent to the cattle yards I would find it so much easier to maintain security over our pedigree Charolais in the farm-yard and adjoining fields, but perhaps of even more importance I would be on hand to monitor the calving of valuable pedigree cows instead of having to get in a vehicle every time I wanted to see them. I presented the above reasons for building at Hall Farm and suggested to the planning officer that if we built accommodation onto the end of my 93 year old mother's cottage, that was adjacent to the farmyard, it would enable her to continue living in her own home to the end of her days. She had become increasingly frail necessitating Pat to travel to her house on a very regular basis to supply her with all her meals and generally care for her. We thought that attaching an annex apart from any other farming considerations, provided the perfect solution as it meant that there would always be someone on hand to care for my mother's needs. Regrettably all of this fell on deaf ears with the planning officer, who made us jump through hoops in his efforts to refuse our application.

His first blocking tactic was to make us prove via an ADAS report costing £ 750 that we were viable farmers and not hobbyists. At one point he even proposed that my mother should be moved in to a home in order that we live in her cottage. Fortunately members of the planning committee saw things differently as they unanimously voted to approve the planning proposal and reject the planner's recommendation for refusal at the April meeting.

Builders were engaged; enabling us to commence building work on May 10th when the top soil was stripped from the site enabling the foundations to be dug. Work proceeded apace with Alistair, Adrian and I doing all work within in our capabilities but more importantly overseeing the project and keeping a continuity of tradesmen as we integrated the build with the seasonal farm work. The build went extremely well allowing us to move in during the first week in October. That dovetailed harmoniously with the sale of Ivy House.

A stock farmers greatest fear apart from an outbreak of a virulent disease such as Foot and Mouth disease is - fire. Shortly after midnight on January 22nd 2002 our worst fears were realised when arsonists, who were later caught but not convicted, set fire to a seven bay Dutch barn full of hay and straw at Hill House Farm alongside Pedlar Lane. Our cattle are all housed in roofed cattle buildings for the six winter months, when hay and straw for eating and bedding is stored under cover, in adjacent Dutch Barns to keep it dry. We live in dread of hearing the sound of fibre cement roofs exploding as the contents of a barn burst into flames, and are faced with the horror of fire engulfing the animals who not only place their complete trust in us but over the years become a part of the family.

A near gale was blowing from the south west that night which fanned the flames towards an adjacent cattle building that held 30 breeding bulls. Quick thinking on Alistair's part in using the fork lift to move flaming big round bales of hay and straw as they collapsed from within the interior of the Dutch Barn prevented any serious injury to the cattle though placing him in considerable personal danger. It was touch and go for some time as crazed animals frantic with fear milled around in the smoke filled adjacent buildings, as the fire roared into a white hot intensity. It twisted the metal girders into amazing shapes and caused a constant bombardment of fibre cement roof particles to rain down on to the nearby roofs of the buildings above the animals and neighbours' bungalows. The fire brigades strategy was to allow the bales to burn throughout the night whilst they continually worked in great clouds of smoke and steam, spraying water onto the hot walls and roofs of nearby buildings. As dawn broke the horror of what had happened became all too apparent, what had been a 7 bay Dutch Barn full of hay and straw the night before, was now a tangled mass of blackened steel with wisps' of grey smoke still rising from the mound of black ash. The barn of course was completely destroyed along with all the straw and feed that we needed to feed the cattle for the remainder of the winter, resulting in more than £45,000 of damage. We decided to rebuild the replaced barn at another yard well away from a public road.

Having witnessed the frightening effects of a fire of this magnitude I fail to understand the mentality of the arsonists who were responsible for creating this carnage, with the very real possibility that, but for Alistairs quick thinking, could have resulted in either a horrible death or serious injury to innocent animals.

The next major expansion occurred in 2002, less than a year after our purchase of Red Leas Farm, when Eastfield Farm in Grimoldby came on to the market. Although over the previous 6 years we had fully integrated Red Leas and Ivy House into the farm we were definitely not anxious to purchase more land, let alone another 300 acre farm, particularly as we were just finalising the purchase of Red Leas, but as the farm abutted our land at Ivy House we placed a bid not really expecting it to be high enough but eventually after negotiation, much to our surprise it was accepted. Over the intervening years Eastfield has formed an important element of the farm which has given us the necessary acreage to continually make greater use of the latest machinery.

Front page of the Louth Leader January 23rd 2002.

CHAPTER 16
Light Refreshment

Over the years I have sold and delivered a great many bulls to purchaser's farms throughout the United Kingdom with the result that I have met a great many interesting characters and encountered many interesting experiences meeting farmers in all sorts of situations on their farms and in their homes.

Take the case of a bull that I was delivering to a new purchaser, near Nottingham, around Easter time one year. On my arrival at his farm I was dismayed to be confronted by a morass of ankle deep mud, so extensive, that in addition to completely covering the farmyard, extended close to the back door of their house. The purchaser requested that I back my trailer, containing the bull, up to a stable on the far side of the farmyard where he wanted to house the bull. I became acutely aware that if I wasn't careful I could easily get stuck by grounding my Land Rover and trailer in one of the water filled pools, whose depth I could only guess at. However I successfully completed the manoeuvre, but when I expressed my misgivings to him about the amount of manure in the stable where his new bull was going to be housed, he gave me an assurance that as soon as the weather improved the bull would be turned out to grass. So reasonably satisfied with his explanation I closed the stable door firmly behind the bull and accepted his invitation to accompany him back to the house in order that he could settle the account and deal with the necessary paperwork. I followed the farmer and his three teenage children, who had joined their father to take a look at their new arrival, as they all retreated across the muddy yard and entered the back door of the house into a small, low roofed, scullery. Out of respect for the farmer's wife and the cleanliness of her home I removed my muddy wellington boots at the door, although I noted that the farmer and the rest of his family failed to remove their muddy boots as they passed into a small living room leaving a trail of mud on a carpet of indeterminate pattern. The farmer's wife, who was standing almost out of sight, in the dimly lit scullery, made me jump as I concentrated on where to place my feet, when she said in such an authoritarian manner that didn't invite a negative reply, "You'll have a cup of tea"! I couldn't help but notice that in spite of the poor light she had a two gallon clear plastic jug standing in front of her that had streaks of a creamy white tide mark extending for perhaps three inches down the inside of the jug to a level slightly above a pale greeny-blue liquid, which left me in little doubt what that would be used for. However the statement had been made in such a matter of fact manner that it would have been churlish to decline her offer. No sooner did I sit down in the living room than a Jack Russell grabbed the end of one of my socks in its teeth and with a mixture of frantic barking and snarls tried its utmost to remove it. The farmer's wife entered the living room and wordlessly plonked half a dozen mugs onto the table. She retreated back into the scullery, only to emerge once again gripping a large brown metal teapot that would not have disgraced a large gathering in a village hall, whereupon she proceeded to fill all the mugs with tea in a continuous pouring motion not bothering to pause between individual mugs. Without a word being spoken she left the room and passed into the back room once again, only to re-emerge into the living room, but this time clutching the big plastic jug with the funny coloured milk which I had spotted earlier, then without any preamble she proceeded to top up the mugs using the same continuous labour saving action. Not wishing to offend my client I closed my eyes and swallowed trying not to dwell on how long the greeny blue liquid had been in that plastic jug. Not the best cuppa I have ever tasted!

On another occasion, I took a bull to a bachelor farmer one particularly hot day in the middle of July, when I had to pass through an extremely untidy farmyard to reach the backdoor of the farmhouse and reluctantly accept the offer of the obligatory cup of tea. Although the summer's day was still and oppressive with dazzling sunshine striking down from a brilliant blue sky, I thought I could detect a peculiar humming noise that I found hard to place as we approached the back door to the house. All of a sudden I realised that the noise must be coming from within.

I followed the farmer through the back door into an outer scullery type of room that contained a display of Victorian domestic and farm tools that wouldn't have disgraced a farm museum. The sound increased in volume to a low pitched drone. Owing to the low light levels, the next room that we passed into was even murkier than the first dingy room. A solitary low wattage electric light bulb augmented what little light percolated the grimey north facing window. The room doubled as kitchen, living room and office, judging by the piles of dusty looking papers stacked haphazardly not only on the table but on every other flat area that provided a level surface, including that of an upright piano that must have been many years since it had last played a note. A pile of grey blankets were loosely draped over an ancient chaise longue, which indicated that the room could even have served as his bed room as well. It was even hotter inside the darkened interior of the house than the sweltering heat outside, when I noticed that the extra warmth probably had something to do with a coal fire burning steadily in the grate. I soon discovered that the source of the noise that I had heard outside of the house was coming from this very room where I was destined to have my cup of tea. I had noticed a strong reasty* bacon smell when I had entered the outer scullery which wasn't unusual as most folk still cured their own bacon at that time. Therefore I wasn't surprised to see joints of salt meat hanging from the bacon hooks on the ceiling, but what I wasn't prepared for was the hundreds of iridescent blue bottles swirling and diving around the light bulb in a vain attempt to escape. My stomach was starting to heave at the prospect of the cup of tea but I was relieved that his refreshment didn't extend to a ham sandwich.

One day in the spring of 1988 I received a phone call from a farmer on Bodmin Moor in Cornwall who was interested in purchasing one of our poll Charolais bulls. I invited him to view our herd up here in Lincolnshire, but he said he had never travelled out of Cornwall, so I suggested that he receive one of our videos to view the bulls.

"No, I can`t do that", he said.

"Why is that"? I asked.

I ain`t got a video",

"Perhaps you can view it on a friends video recorder". I responded

"That's impossible, I don`t know anyone whose got one, just bring me a Polled Bull mister".

As I was already taking another bull to South Devon I decided to take another one along at the same time and extend my journey to his farm on Bodmin Moor which I eventually reached by driving down a very narrow track little wider than my trailer with a steep drop running along one side. After some distance I came to a group of disconsolate hens scratching in a patch of scrubby grass in front of a range of dilapidated and seemingly ruined farm buildings. Just as I was beginning to think that this was a

* reasty: rancid

180

wind up, I was astonished to see a bent old man supported by a stick in either hand emerge from within the entrance of one of the partially collapsed sheds. Having announced who I was and established that he was the man that I had spoken too, the old chap showed me the well bedded part of one shed that he had prepared for his new bull, with clean drinking water in a trough and a bundle of hay in the rack above a wooden feed trough. I was delighted that in spite of the bulls long journey that he calmly walked off the trailer and immediately started to eat the hay. After handing me a cheque the old chap was clearly delighted with his new purchase as he stood alongside his new bull and rubbed him above his shoulders with one of his sticks. The bull unconcernedly munched away on some sweet smelling hay. He rang me a few months later to say how delighted he was with his new bull and thanked me for being so trusting.

From my view point, up here on Conscience Hill looking towards the marsh villages all these many years later I remember a rich kaleidoscope of village characters who lived their entire lives in this relatively small part of rural Lincolnshire.

Bicycles that used to provide many people's sole means of transport 50 years ago, carried the additional benefit of allowing people to stop and have a chat with their neighbours and pass on the latest village gossip. Take Bob Parker for example: he was a lean framed exceptionally strong hard working man, a bachelor who lived by himself in Fleet House down Pick Hill lane, in the adjacent village of Grimoldby. I frequently met Bob cycling up Stewton lane with his 12 bore shotgun strapped to the crossbar, as he made his way to one of his relative's fields, hoping to shoot something that he could take home to eat. Perhaps because he led such a solitary life Bob loved to have a chat. In anticipation of having a talk with a passerby he would dismount his cycle in good time, then with a twinkle in his eye and a broad smile he had the ability to beguile the most reticent of the people that he met. After adjusting the hessian haversack that he habitually wore around his neck to a more comfortable position, he would lean over his cycle frame and his cheerful face would explode in a broad grin as it prefaced his latest tale with, "ev yer eard", and then laughingly carry on to remark about his observations on the current or expected weather, followed by his latest shooting accomplishment. *"Ay ive shot fower long tailed uns ower the last couple o weeks" adding, "yur knaw town fowks let um go on the sand hills an then they, (the foxes) travel back*

Clearing farm yard manure and loading into an 18 ton trailer

up the Greyfleet". He was referring to shooting foxes along the banks of the Greyfleet beck that passed along the northern boundary of his field which lay behind his house. This waterway, similar to the South Dike at Red Leas is one of several waterways crossing the marsh to the sea. It consequently serves as a main highway for foxes to travel between the wolds and the coast. Although Bob owned a couple of fields he decided to rent them out, preferring to earn his living working either at piecework rates or being employed on a casual 'day rate' basis. Prior to the ending of the dyke reed mowing auction, at Saltfleetby's Prussian Queen, in the early 60s, Bob in common with men like Arthur Benton would bid against each other in a Dutch Auction to mow the various Drainage Board Drains for the lowest price. Each drain had a separate name, such as the Mar Dyke that passed in front of The Prussian Queen. It was incredibly hard work as it involved standing on the steep drain sides placing one leg precariously higher than the other, whilst at the same time, wielding a scythe to mow the reeds growing not only in the bed of the drain but also the tough grass and reeds that grew on either side of the bank. By using a combination of a special, long handled, gathering rake with extra long teeth and a wide tined fork, the mown grass and reeds were gathered together and hauled on to the bank top.

In the days before combine harvesters became widespread in the 1950s, threshing machines travelled from farm to farm to thresh farmers' corn. Consequently additional hired labour was required to supplement regular farm labour on threshing days. Bob found regular employment throughout the winter months either forking sheaves on the corn stack or stacking the freshly threshed straw. In more recent years threshing sets have became confined to nostalgic exhibition days when members of an older generation reminisce on how threshing used to be done, "in the good old days". As a free agent with no family or business ties he loved to travel, when if the whim took him he might suddenly decide that he would like to go to New Zealand or perhaps Canada having distant relations in both countries. In 1961 my travels in New Zealand brought me to Taranaki in the North Island and gave me an opportunity to use the address that Bob had provided, so that I might look up Mr Ian Bond, one of his distant relatives that he used to visit. The Bonds informed me that Bob would rarely write to say that he was coming, let alone ask if it was convenient. Just like a will o' the wisp he would suddenly turn up and stay with them for in some cases several weeks assisting them with whatever work they were carrying out at that time. They said that he would rarely reveal when he might be leaving, perhaps because he was unsure himself until the eve of his departure, when he would announce, "I'll be off tomorrow." In spite of his strange ways the Bonds said that they thoroughly enjoyed his company and were always sorry to see him leave. Bob was always a font of outrageous actions and statements in the face of officialdom. His unique sense of innocent humour was graphically illustrated when he once accompanied our local Mid Marsh YFC on a day trip to Scarborough. He donned a tiny funfair policeman's helmet that perched rather ridiculously on the top of his head. With an an open necked shirt that seemed to be resigned to the impossibility of containing the hairy rug trying to escape from somewhere within he set about directing traffic through the milling crowds of holidaymakers who thronged the seafront. He carried such a serious demeanour on his face that in spite of looking quite ridiculous, people religiously observed his hand signals that were delivered in such a professional manner. No he hadn't been drinking as he was completely teetotal!

On another memorable occasion I recall a training course being held in one of the lecture rooms at nearby RAF Manby for the Lincolnshire Police Special Constabulary of which both he and I were members. The course was designed to instruct the 20 or so assembled special constables, who all lived and worked in the Louth area, on the way that ejector seats worked and what to do if we were the first on the scene of a crashed aircraft. Manby at the time was a very important training base, resulting in a great deal of aerial activity as trainee pilots did circuits of the airfield, doing landings and takeoffs, with usually half a dozen aircraft flying the circuit at any one time. The RAF training officer had spent most of the evening demonstrating in great clarity by means of film and a real pilot's ejector seat the correct procedure to be adopted in disarming the ejector seat mechanism in order that the pilot could be safely released. He emphasised how vital it was that we had to be extremely careful not to activate the explosive device under the seat otherwise the pilot and ourselves would be rocketed several hundred feet into the air. After more than two hours of detailed instruction he asked in summary, "Does everyone now completely understand how to disarm an ejector seat if you are the first on the scene of a crashed aircraft?" There was a chorus murmuring in the affirmative. "Now" he said turning to Bob, "Should an aircraft crash-land in the field behind your house what would you do?" to which Bob replied, "Run like ell."

I was never quite sure if the answer was intended to deflate the RAF officer's pomposity, as I am certain that he would do his utmost to assist anyone in distress.

Bob was especially good company at all village social events, when his booming authoritarian voice would generally preface a statement with, "well'll yer see". He regularly attended whist drives throughout the winter months as he enjoyed the warm rooms and companionship of other players that he could talk to on cold, winters evenings.

On one infamous occasion, one of the weekly winter whist drives was taking place at North Cockerington School in aid of the Lindsey Blind

Society. The assembled players broke for a supper interval midway through the event, when cakes, sandwiches and tea were brought to the quartets of two men and two women seated around a number of collapsible card tables. Suddenly Bob sneezed and reached into one of the pockets of his voluminous coat for a handkerchief, but instead by mistake - "maybe" - pulled out a dead rat by its tail. The ladies screamed as they pushed back their chairs and in the process upturned several of the flimsy card tables distributing half eaten sandwiches and angel cakes amidst cups of tea across the floor.

There was rarely a dull moment when Bob Parker was part of the party. Regrettably towards the end of his life he picked up a foot infection, and rather than see a doctor, perhaps because he had never consulted a doctor in his entire life, attempted to treat it with dock leaves and other herbal remedies. Unfortunately the problem got worse. It resulted in him being admitted to hospital where gangrene was diagnosed, making it neccessary to amputate his leg below the knee. I visited him in hospital when he assured me that he would soon be mobile again, as he did not care for confined, hospital accommodation. Following the fitting of a prosthetic leg it wasn't too long before he was cycling again with his trusty shotgun strapped to his crossbar, and his foot and leg firmly wedged in a pair of wellington boots.

My gaze is once again attracted to a line of cars, looking like a row of metallic beads, as their drivers return home after a day's work in Louth which reminds me of Foggy who spent his days watching Mr Green's cows grazing the roadside verges between Keddington and Pub Corner. He was a slightly built middle aged man with a bent, wiry frame, and walked with a stumbling gait, delivering his words rather indistinctly. As children we found his eccentric behaviour somewhat intimidating, when we either walked or cycled past him. At unpredictable moments he would twirl his whip, that seemed to be permanently in his grasp, and then with the most amazing dexterity flick his wrist allowing a length of sinewy cord to snake past us with the leather thong at the end of it cracking like a revolver inches from our noses. Of course he had refined his whip technique over the years of doing the job so that by using a minimum of effort he could draw a wayward cow smartly back in line without actually having to walk across the road to her.

Today's vastly increased traffic volumes with so many impatient drivers sat behind the wheel has rendered the practice of grazing roadside verges quite impractical. Cows tend to roam at will from one side of the road to the other completely oblivious to traffic and would consequently soon cause an accident. As I reminisce about old Foggy and his way of life 50 years ago I ponder whether society has really moved on, especially when I consider that productive employment had been found in those days to utilise his limited talents and provide him with a healthy outdoor life. In addition, allowing his cows to graze the coarse roadside grasses and other dominant roadside vegetation had two other important functions. Firstly the cows trimmed the grass short eliminating the need to mow the verges for visibility and secondly it opened up the sward so that a profusion of smaller wild flowers such as vetches and trefoils were able to flower and flourish. It may be that in years to come, with the advent of a world food shortage looming that we will once again need to produce food from all available ground, including roadside verges.

The marsh had many wonderful characters who didn't suffer fools gladly, take Sam Cook for example. His dour countenance gave little indication of his true emotions when dealing with officialdom. He usually wore an old raincoat that stretched to within a few inches of the ground. At first glance it appeared to be camouflaged but was in fact stained with mud and a lifetime spent working with livestock. Buttons that had long since disappeared had been substituted by a length of well used baler twine that encircled his girth, whilst his flat cap had lost the button holding the front peak. Sam in common a with many farmers of his generation wanted "a good deal" when it came to spending money, so it was with some trepidation that a Louth garage salesman met him, in the early afternoon, following Louth market to discuss the purchase of a pickup truck. After protracted negotiations when the debate had ranged over such mundane topics as how much would the salesman knock off if a front passenger mat was omitted, or what reduction might he give if the vehicle was not washed before it was delivered, the exasperated salesman finally agreed to Sam's bid when he declared.

"Alright Mr Cook we'll have a deal," to which Sam responded, "nar wot will yer knock of if I eve two".

The salesman, it's reliable reported counted silently to ten and then transferred Sam to a colleague claiming a bad attack of migraine coming on. On another occasion, Sam was returning home to lunch, on a particularly hot summer's day, when he came upon a smartly dressed young man bending over the ditch that passed alongside his farmyard. For many generations of the Cook family, the ditch had been the natural outlet for rainwater falling on their farmyard along with any liquid draining from their farm buildings. Over the years with little natural flow of water a deposit of black sludge built up in the bottom of the ditch, but as they lived hundreds of yards from the nearest habitation it was affecting no one else. Sam observed the man, in his stylish pin stripe suit, white shirt and polished black shoes, for some minutes as the official repeatedly cast a glass vessel attached to a piece of cord into the murky water and studiously examined the contents. Curiosity getting the better of him, he ambled up to the man who was intently examining another jar of liquid and exclaimed, "Yer woant ketch owt in thear mester", The man recovered himself from the dyke bank and by way of explanation declared, "I'm from the council and I have to inform you that this ditch is heavily polluted so I'm going to give you 36 hours to cleanse it". Mr Cook who had little time for sartorially dressed officials pondered this statement for some time before remarking "I've got ar betta idea".

"What's that?" said the council man.

"Mek it er munth" said Sam, with a whimsical expression.

Charlie Ogdon, always referred to as Oggie, was a unique, marshland character whose lean frame carried little surplus flesh and a sallow complexion that very rarely broke into a smile. He had a reputation for being exceptionally careful with his money by not spending a penny if a halfpenny would do. His long greying hair was slicked back, accentuating his lean hungry looking features which were habitually cloaked in a week's growth of black stubble that grew in the facial canyons of his craggy grey face. On one occasion, a nearby neighbour had lost a ram from his flock of sheep when he came to count them one Friday morning. He searched backwards and forwards around the field, but there was not the slightest sign of the ram or how the animal could possibly have escaped from the field. Completely mystified as to the rams whereabouts he went to Louth market as was his norm on a Friday. As he walked by the pens of sheep, that were for sale later that morning, he spotted his missing ram in a pen of other sheep, and asked the clerk whose sheep they were. He was informed that they were Mr. Ogdon's, who when confronted, gave a lame excuse claiming that the ram must have somehow unbeknown to him got amongst his sheep then he had failed to notice it amongst the 10 other ewes that he had taken to market that day. The considerate neighbour, not wishing to create trouble, informed Oggie, that provided the ram was returned to his field forthwith that would be the end of the matter.

Oggie had a reputation for living at the expense of others, particularly where the feeding of his stock was concerned, as I was to discover for myself on a later occasion. We had recently purchased an isolated field, down a track some distance from the home farm, which we seldom visited during the winter months. We were totally unaware at the time of Oggie's roaming sheep, until one of our new neighbours remarked that as our sheep had eaten all the grass in our new field were we going to move them soon. I pointed out to him that we didn't own sheep, so they must belong to somebody else. My new neighbour soon informed me of Oggie's husbandry credentials, and that the offending animals would almost certainly be his. When I inspected our field I discovered that it was full of Oggie's sheep and they had completely stripped the field bare of the grass that we would need for our cattle when they were turned out in the spring. I soon discovered that Oggie had made no attempt to fence his sheep in his adjoining field. It was confirmation of what my new neighbour had told me, that Oggie rarely fenced around any of his fields, resulting in sheep frequently getting out and foraging other peoples land. Uncertain of where Oggie lived I consulted the phone book only to discover that he wasn't listed, so I approached my new neighbour who gave me directions to locate Oggie's isolated house.

The February day was dank and foggy with a penetrating cold that seemed to percolate into my very bones as I found Oggie's house someway down an isolated track. The mist swirled revealing a two storied brick building, with peeling paintwork, and a single, external door. Everywhere appeared deserted with any pretence at maintaining a garden long since abandoned to the combined onslaughts of twitch grass and nettles that were attempting to cloak an onslaught of rusting obsolete farm machinery. Forlornly I knocked on the door to the screech of a distressed curlew lost in the fog on the out marsh, when suddenly a muffled voice from inside said,

"Who is it?"

After identifying who I was, the distant voice said "Come in". I squeezed my way through a door that I could only partially open due to a pile of chains stored in the narrow hallway immediately behind it. I was confronted by a flight of bare wooden stairs that led up to the next floor when I heard the disembowelled voice say, "Come up but mind how you go". The stairs had a chicane of various tools and smaller items of farm machinery placed on alternate sides of the steep narrow stairway. It gave me the impression that they just might have been deliberately arranged in such a manner in order to give an early warning of unexpected visitors. With little natural light percolating the gloomy stairwell I carefully ascended the steep steps. In itself this was a tricky operation as a poorly placed foot was liable to dislodge one of the stored items and precipitate an avalanche. At the top of the stairs I was confronted by a small landing with 3 or 4 doors leading off to various upstairs rooms. Oggie sat huddled in an army greatcoat on a chair that was drawn up to a small card table piled high with part used jars of jam and various tins exposing myriad alien contents.

In the small igloo like space where little of the meagre winter light penetrated, I breezily explained to Oggie that I had tried to contact him by phone but couldn't find his number in the telephone directory.

"It's in the book" he confidently explained, "look I'le show yer".

I followed him into an adjacent uncarpeted room where a single window overlooked the bleak windswept marsh to the north. Little of the dismal late afternoon light passed through a couple of green stained panes that revealed evidence of how tentacles of slime had slid triffid like from the glass onto the window frame. The room carried still more examples of long redundant farm hand tools that bore ample witness to the way that wood worms, if left undisturbed, could pursue their relentless task of reducing anything composed of wood back to dust. "Ay, eres the phone book," Oggie explained triumphantly pointing to a pile of telephone directories, then selecting one from the pile opened it to find his entry. I said "it didn't really matter as I was here now in any case".

I was confident that he knew why I had come to see him, but he persisted in delaying my inevitable questions about his sheep as he studiously poured through more directories before saying resignedly,

"Well it should be in", continuing to flick over more pages yet still failed to find his entry. When I was eventually able to raise the issue of his sheep grazing our land, Oggie claimed that they couldn't possibly be his sheep, then rather in the manner of Shylock declared, "But if they are mine then it'l be the fost tem I've iver known um git out."

One of farming's great features is that most business transactions involving either selling produce, or purchasing new machinery is conducted on the basis that a verbal agreement is binding. It's therefore unsurprising that having spoken to a farmer who I may never have previously met, I have been prepared to take animals to the far side of the country and take away their uncleared cheque in payment. Over and again I have been touched by the humble homes where many genuine farmers live, wanting only the very best for the animals under their care. I was moved by the reaction of one of our customers two years ago.

The gentleman had bought one of our bulls some ten years earlier only to find that through no fault of his own his cattle had contracted the dreaded "Foot and Mouth" disease when the virus escaped from the lab at Pirbright. The ministry decreed that the bull along with the rest of his cattle had to be slaughtered immediately. With tears running down his face he explained how the bull that he called "Neddy" would run across the field to greet him and take a sugar lump from his hand. He told me how he spent many hours with the animal and described him as one of the best friends that he had ever had, and that he would gladly have given all the compensation the ministry grudgingly gave him in return for having his friend back. He related a harrowing tale on the way that rough abattoir workers had been only partially successful as they attempted to shoot Neddy in the field with a captive bolt gun whilst the desperate animal had sought sanctuary with him.

FIGURE 13.

Geological Schematic
Saltfleetby "B" Site Extension

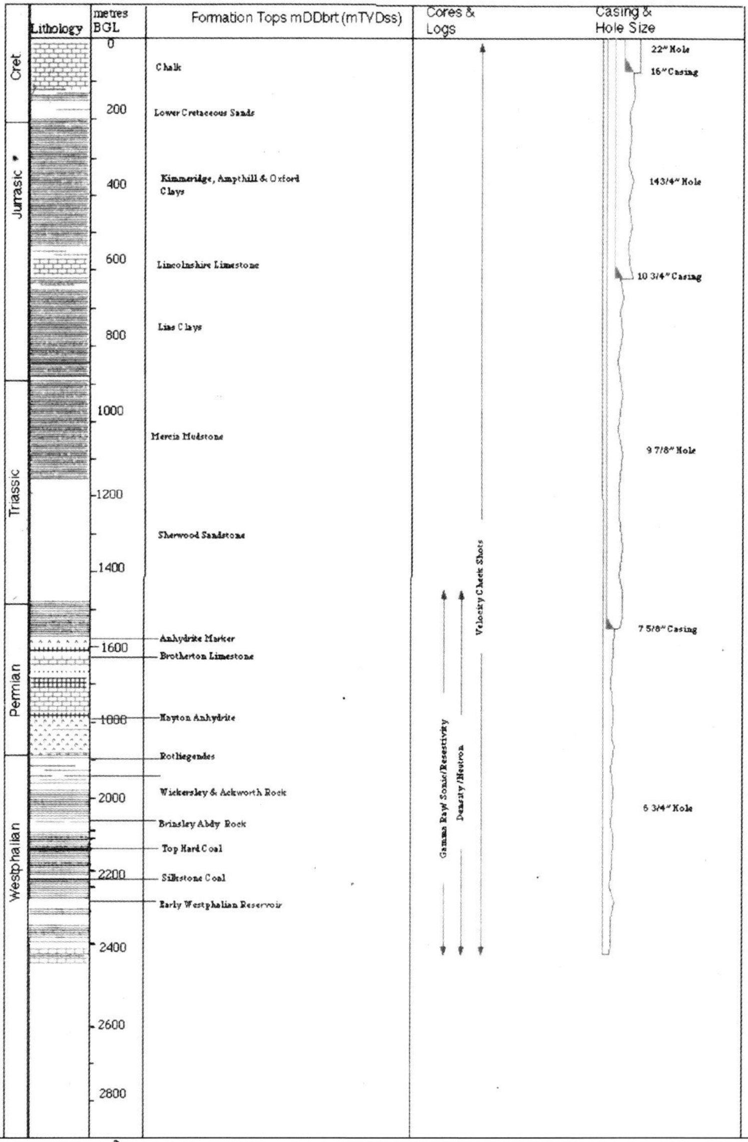

Lithology	metres BGL	Formation Tops mDDbrt (mTVDss)	Cores & Logs	Casing & Hole Size
Cret	0			22" Hole
		Chalk		16" Casing
	200	Lower Cretaceous Sands		
Jurasic *	400	Kimmeridge, Ampthill & Oxford Clays		14 3/4" Hole
	600	Lincolnshire Limestone		10 3/4" Casing
	800	Lias Clays		
Triassic	1000	Mercia Mudstone		9 7/8" Hole
	1200			
		Sherwood Sandstone		
	1400			
Permian	1600	Anhydrite Marker / Brotherton Limestone		7 5/8" Casing
	1800	Kayton Anhydrite		
		Rotliegendes		
Westphalian	2000	Wickersley & Ackworth Rock		6 3/4" Hole
		Brinsley Abdy Rock		
		Top Hard Coal		
	2200	Silkstone Coal		
		Early Westphalian Reservoir		
	2400			
	2600			
	2800			

Logs column vertical labels: Gamma Ray/ Sonic/Resistivity, Density/Neutron, Velocity Check Shots

A profile of the geology under the Lincolnshire Marsh. Roc oil

CHAPTER 17
Bill and George

"Come ya quick, Bills deeing", George Hoyes managed to gasp between gulps of air, as in a state of near panic he beat his fists against the front door of our house one bright spring morning in 1969 some 5 years after we were married.

Bill and George Hoyes were two unmarried brothers close to 70 years of age, who had recently retired from their farm at Stewton Newkin and moved down to a bungalow a couple of miles away in Grimoldby where a distant relation who lived next door to them was able to cook and care for their home. The brothers two sisters Maggie and Louie who had also never married, had predeceased them only a year or two earlier.

This was but the latest in a series of desperate calls for help that went back over many years from a family who led very reclusive lives yet regularly called on our family as their nearest neighbours in time of trouble.

Judging by the way that Georges bike was sprawled in the hedge beside our drive all manner of likely tragic scenarios started to flash through my head of what Pat and I were likely to expect. George's speech, that was never easy to follow at the best of times was now almost incoherent.

I drove as fast as I dare down the lanes to their new house with George hyperventilating in the rear seat behind me as he mangled his words between great gasps of air, *"Can y a r goa fe st er Ral uf eal sue un be deed"*.

Pat urged me on fearing that whatever we found at Grimoldby would soon be compounded by an additional fatality in the back of the car.

Fortunately on this occasion to our great relief Bill had merely fainted and was sitting reasonably comfortable in an easy chair wondering what all the fuss was about.

From my viewpoint looking south I can see the mile long straight road of Stewton Lane running from Hill House Farm at its eastern end to the parish boundary of Stewton Newkin where the Hoyes family used to live at its western end.

I can see an oil tanker lorry moving slowly up the road to collect a load of crude oil from the two oil wells that have recently been drilled opposite where the Hoyes farmhouse used to stand.

The metalled road used to end at the entrance to the Hoyes's Farmyard where it then devolved into a rough cart track that passed on the South side of first the farmyard and then after another 25 yards passed in front of the farmhouse's unkempt garden. After another 40 yards, the track passed the entrance to our forty acre field and then devolved into an overgrown wilderness of shrubby blackthorn bushes and briars; however old maps show the track continuing across the boundaries of fields to Stewton Village about a mile away.

As the arm of one of the nodding donkeys at the end of the road relentlessly moves up and down pumping oil from the depths of the earth, I wonder what the Hoyes family who were living and farming adjacent to the drilling site until 1964, would have made of these twenty first century developments.

The four unmarried Hoyes brothers and sisters lived in what I always thought, in my time as a child, to be an intimidating old farm house as it lay partially shrouded by a giant weeping ash tree that gave it a Dickensian forbidding appearance, particularly in the dark dank days of winter. The farmhouse was a traditional Lincolnshire 18th century dwelling built of dark red brick and an almost black slate roof with a substantial chimney block at both gables. At the back, the roof sloped down over a lean-to extension that accommodated a scullery and washhouse that rather like a demilitarised zone at a border crossing had to be passed through before entering the inner sanctum of the house. Originally the front door, positioned in the middle of the house facing south, would have provided a grand entrance as it opened on to a path leading across the garden to a gate fronting the track 40 yards away. The door looked as though it had remained unused for decades as peeling paint and bleached woodwork were partially obscured by dead grass and weeds that shielded the doors lower part. So it was little wonder that by abandoning the front of the house to a veritable wilderness of nettles and other persistent weeds that access to the property was gained by passing first through the stack yard and then round the corner of a brick barn to the back door of the house.

The windows were draped in sombre coloured curtains with the bottom half of the downstairs ones cloaked with net curtains in order that total privacy could be maintained. As much of the paint had long since peeled from the surrounding frames the woodwork had taken on an overall grey hue which accentuated the houses forbidding appearance.

In spite of walking with a pronounced stoop Bill was the family spokesman and decision maker, whilst his moustachioed brother George was much more retiring, and could generally be found shyly laughing in the background, whilst his brother conducted a conversation.

The two sisters Louie and Maggie kept house and it was only on very rare occasions that they ventured from the family home.

From time to time my parents instructed me to bike the mile length of Stewton Lane to relay a telephone message as the Hoyes family didn't own a phone. I remember that I used to walk through the farmyard with a great deal of trepidation because even when I thought that I had succeeded in reaching the back door of the house undetected, I might suddenly be ambushed by two or three of their sheep dogs that would materilize as if by magic. On the rare occasions when I thought that I had out witted them I would suddenly spot one of the dogs out of the corner of my eye, partially camouflaged by a pile of loose straw, lying flat to the ground and completely motionless in the way that only sheepdogs know how. As I approached the backdoor to the house I would continue to keep a wary eye on the dog. Although it was still keeping flat to the ground it seemed snake like to imperceptibly creep forwards, then as I turned to knock on the door with a clenched fist it had a habit of shooting forward with lightening speed giving my bottom a sharp nip as it attacked me from the rear.

I remember that I generally had to pick my way through a motley selection of varying sized tabby cats clustered around numerous saucers and dishes by the back door, as they waited in keen anticipation for their next feed. I could see where the brown paint hadn't already peeled off the back door and surrounding frame, the woodwork was deeply riven with countless claw marks inflicted over the years by generations of their cats and dogs.

I usually had to knock a number of times on the door in order that they could hear me as the backdoor of the house led into a scullery with another door leading into the kitchen cum living room beyond, but whilst I waited I had to keep a watchful eye on the sheepdogs who by this stage were barking furiously rather like the hounds of the Baskervilles as they formed a semi circle to cover any escape that I had in mind.

After what seemed like an age I thought I could detect the muffled sound of a chair leg scraping over a hard floor from inside the house, followed by a key turning in the lock as the back door opened a couple of inches to reveal part of the face of one of the two portly sisters. *"Hew iz it Mag?"* I could hear someone call from inside the house as I caught a fleeting glimpse of the other sister peering furtively around the door frame from the gloomy interior. *"Wi its Ral-ulf"*, Louie replied opening the door a little wider, *"whit ar yer brut uz"*. *"Mother says that Briggs, (livestock transporters from Louth), have phoned up to say that they will collect your sheep for tomorrows market at half past seven."* I explained.

On rare occasions, particularly if it was wet, or blowing a howling gale I was invited to *"cum in."* Passing through the scullery with its brown glazed sink forlornly illuminated by a meagre amount of light passing through a small paned north facing window, I could see an array of old heavily stained and torn coats lining the pegs on two of the walls. An assortment of metal buckets, some of which were partially full of heavily soiled eggs stood on the worn brick floor to the left of the door, whilst an amazing selection of footwear lined the perimeter of the other walls. Dirt engrained Wellington boots and brown polished market boots stood beside once black leather work boots that had now adopted a universal grey colour accrued from years of combining mud with cow manure. Highly polished knee high brown leather leggings hung from pegs on the wall, and further back on the shelves that surrounded the room I could see a vast assortment of other boots and ladies shoes, some of which, judging by their grey mouldy appearance must have been there since the time of their parents in Victorian times.

I was never invited to tread a deal more than a couple of paces into the living room, which was dominated in its centre by a substantially constructed, late Victorian, mahogany table supported on heavily carved turned legs with white caster wheels. I remember the table was always draped in a heavy dark brown cloth that resembled a blanket, although where it overhung the sides, a pattern in a different shade of brown appeared to have been embroided along the edges.

The poorly lit room was illuminated by a brass oil lamp suspended by a hook attached to a wooden beam that ran across the width of the ceiling. The flickering light from the oil lamp illuminated a solidly built mahogany sideboard which dominated one wall, stretching from the floor to within a few inches of the ceiling, with the flat top serving as the repository for piles of accumulated farm documents. In addition to the doorway where I was standing two further doors led out of the room with all three continuing the same depressing dark brown colour scheme as though they had pledged long ago to refrain from using any other colour. Little light percolated through the net curtains of the single south facing window, which in turn was framed by dark brown floor length curtains. Stretching across the major portion of the remaining wall was a black kitchen range with a few smouldering embers in the fire grate producing narrow trails of smoke that climbed lazily into the soot encrusted chimney.

Isolated as they were with very few visitors to bring them news I was always quizzed on a whole raft of seemingly mundane topics. *"Eve yer brock up frum sckoo-al yit."* Or *"Ez yer faitha tond eny beast out yit."*

The Hoyes brothers must have been one of the last farms in the area to regularly use Shire horses for farm work when their animal horse power was supplemented by an aged, spud wheeled standard Fordson tractor. In the mid 50's as a result no doubt of seeing our new Ferguson tractors, they decided to purchase one themselves, which for the first time gave them mobility on public roads, so that it became a common sight on Louth market day to see hump-backed Bill behind the tractor steering wheel, with his legs splayed on either side of the transmission as he chugged along the road little faster than a brisk walking pace. Brother George had to be content in facing backwards as he perched uncomfortably behind Bill on the hard coiled spring, which formed the top of the three point linkage system, with both of his feet propped for support at either end of the swinging draw bar.

They had a reputation for 'never spending a penny when a ha'penny would do' and had no trust in banks as they operated their business on a largely cash basis.

On one occasion they couldn't open their safe, so in desperation they called in Fred Phillipson, the local blacksmith to open it for them.

Fred was escorted into the house and ushered up stairs where he found the safe positioned in a dark recess at the rear of one of the bedrooms. After a considerable amount of difficulty he eventually managed to free the lock, but before he could so much as open the door half an inch he was unceremoniously bundled out of the room, down the stairs and out of the house, and told that under no circumstances was he to divulge to anyone anything he may have seen.

On many occasions there would be a knock on my parents front door at Hill House, when an agitated Bill would say to my Mother in a plaintive voice, *"Can ya ring Callum (local vet) we 'ev a cow cauving and she cain't get rid on it"*. Alternatively George would appear and irrespective of the time of day or night, say to Mother *"Bill wonts an 'and cauving a cow, can Brian (my Father) gi 'im an 'and"*.

My father would readily accede to these requests –though I never knew them give him more than token thanks for his effort, and there was certainly never any offer of recompense for my father's trouble in getting out of bed in the middle of the night.

Early April would see the two brother's droving a batch of cows down Stewton Road to their grass field in North Cockerington. We always had fair warning that they were coming as soon after they left their farm yard we were able to hear plenty of excited shouting with lots of *"Ho up's"* and *"Git on's"*.

Bill always walked at the back of the drove were he issued a constant stream of commands to his brother, urging him to either "Git on" or "Look out" as George with the task of being front man had the dual responsibility of not only preventing the animals from running on too far ahead, but he also had to stand in the entrance to any fields or houses that did not have a gate to close, As soon as the herd had passed that spot, he had to run past them to get in front once again.

When I was big enough, from the age of ten I had to accompany one of our farm workers droving cattle between our farms remote marsh fields. I hated the task as the job of droving animals always seemed to need doing either on a Saturday morning or during school holidays.

Droving generally commenced early in the morning by collecting a drove of cattle from a field in South Cockerington, and then walking them the 8 miles or so to the farthest field on the farm at Grainthorpe, where they were exchanged with the cattle that had previously been grazing there. The fresh batch of cattle would then be driven the six miles to fields at Saltfleetby where another exchange took place, with the fresh batch of cattle being driven the five miles back home, making a round trip of about 20 miles, but the extra foot work, running backwards and forwards, could be half as much again.

The one hundred and twenty three acres that had been owned and farmed by the Hoyes family were sold in March 1964 for £220 an acre, along with their Lincoln Red cattle, flock of cross bred breeding sheep and poultry reflecting the mixed farms of that period.

Few vehicles other than farm traffic went up Stewton Lane at that time, with the consequence that the County Council highways only metalled the tracks leaving the centre of the road to green over with grass and other weeds.

Close by the farm house stood a small, very exposed two storey cottage that the Scrope Estate built in the late 1800's to house a farm labourer for the Hoyes farm.

From my earliest recollection the house was rented out extremely cheaply, partially because it lacked even the most basic of amenities, but perhaps even more so because of its isolated position as it was over one mile from the nearest bus stop in the village.

To this day I can still visualise the poor widow with a young family, who was the last tenant to live there. With head bent low she trudged past our house often into driving rain gripping two laden baskets of shopping as she embarked on the long walk up to the house.

Both the farm house and the cottage were demolished after the retirement from farming of the Hoyes family when the farmyard and land was amalgamated into Mr. Greenfields much larger adjoining farm in nearby Keddington. The house sites became parts of adjoining fields leaving no trace of the houses that once stood there.

Upon the discovery of oil in 1998 Stewton Road was completely resurfaced making it a high quality level road to service the oil field.

Today the mortal remains of the four unmarried Hoyes brothers and sisters lie in South Cockerington Church yard where the magnificent black Italian marble headstone and surrounding stonework sits rather grandly among some of the more simple sandstone memorials.

During their lifetime they lived very frugally but on death they wanted only the very best.

HIGH PRICES FOR FARM LAND

MORE high prices for arable and grassland in the Louth area were realised at auction sales on Wednesday.

Grassland at Saltfleetby sold for over £240 an acre, while a 122-acre farm at South Cockerington made £220 per acre, and pastures at Mablethorpe over £200. Grassland at Louth sold for over £200 per acre.

At Saltfleetby, 13.262 acres adjoining Fishmeregate Lane, belonging to Miss E. E. W. Michael, were sold for £3,200 to Mrs. Liller, of Legbourne, by Messrs. Masons, Fuller, Chatterton and Haxby. The solicitors were Messrs. Allison and Helmer.

COCKERINGTON FARM

A South Cockerington farm of 112 acres 3 roods 3 perches, Stewton Newkins, was sold by Messrs. Dickinson, Davy and Markham for £27,250 to Mr. Rex Greenfield, Louth.

The land, of which about 58 acres are grass, has been owned and occupied for many years by Messrs. Hoyes Brothers, who are now retiring. The solicitors were Messrs. Allison and Helmer.

SOUTH COCKERINGTON
Near LOUTH, Lincs.

DICKINSON, DAVY & MARKHAM will Sell by Auction at the LOUTH RURAL DISTRICT COUNCIL OFFICES, on

Wednesday, 4 March, 1964

at 2.30 p.m. prompt. (Subject to Conditions to be then produced)

THE

AGRICULTURAL HOLDING

known as

STEWTON NEWKINS

extending to

122 ACRES   3 ROODS   3 PERCHES

of RICH FERTILE LAND, including **58 ACRES GRASSLAND** lying in a ring fence.

As occupied for many years by Messrs. Hoyes Bros., principally as a stock producing farm.

Together with the BRICK AND SLATED FARMHOUSE, containing Entrance Hall, Front Room, Living Room, Scullery, Pantry, Cellar, Four Double Bedrooms, Single Bedroom and Boxroom. Outside Wash-house, Coalhouse, H.C.

BRICK AND TILED COTTAGE containing two Living and three Bedrooms.

Also a substantially constructed set of FARM BUILDINGS, comprising loose boxes, stabling, barn and very good completely covered foldyard in five divisions. Four-bay implement shed.

VACANT POSSESSION ON COMPLETION

Viewing of Farmhouse 2 p.m. to 4 p.m. Wednesdays and Fridays.

Further particulars and permits to view obtainable of the Auctioneers, 2 Nichol Hill, Louth (Tel. 4), and at Brigg and Grimsby, or of the Vendors' Solicitors, Messrs. ALLISON & HELMER, 24 Mercer Row, Louth.

Advert for the Hoyes Bros sale in March 1964 alongside a press report of the sales proceeds.

Site of the Hoyes Farmhouse 2010

CHAPTER 18
Pork and Bacon

As I chew the last mouthful of a ham sandwich I am reminded nostalgically of pig killing and a tradition that has passed into history. It was notable for being perhaps one of the few days in the year when mother was able to command father what to do in the house.

"I'le be theer fost off Munda morning", Arthur Benton the pig killer would respond when father rang him at The Prussian Queen, adding, "doant giv um owt to yet on Sunda neet".

Arthur was a self employed red faced stocky man who until the practice ended in 1961 after 161 years, was one of the last group of hardworking men to take part in Louth Drainage Boards annual Dutch Auction for "dyke letting", when he would bid against other farmers and self employed farm workers for the work of scything reeds from the principle marsh ditches during the late summer months.

The annual event in May was held at the Prussian Queen in Saltfleetby when a perk for the successful bidder for the Mardyke that ran past the front of the public house, was free food and beer on workdays.

During May and June, Arthur led a small gang of sheep clippers, comprising in addition to himself Len Appleby and Harold Stubbs who clipped many of the sheep flocks in the district. It was always called clipping and not shearing in this area, perhaps because Arthur's gang used hand clipping shears as opposed to mechanical shears. During the winter months once he had completed his contractual obligation of reed cutting he was in great demand through the the marsh villages killing pigs, then butchering them the following day.

Until the early 1970s when farming patterns changed and more stringent slaughtering rules were introduced, pretty well every farm kept a few pigs as did the majority of farm workers, who either housed their pig in a sty at the bottom of the garden, which they fed on household waste food, supplemented by cheap meal from their employer, or where it was impractical to do so accepted a pig as part payment from their employer in lieu of wages.

In the vast majority of cases where farmers had insufficient sows for a boar pig of their own they used Henry Parkers or Couplands travelling boar pig service to service their sows.

The pigs were predominantly Large Whites but in later years Dutch Land Race started to be introduced in an effort to make them leaner, but in any event by the time that they were slaughtered they had grown to an immense size frequently attaining weights of up to 50 stones (318 kgs), and as a consequence were very, very fat.

Arthur was not on the phone but could be reliably contacted at his "evening office" in the public bar of the Prussian Queen at Saltfleetby, when pig killing appointments could be made. Our pig killing shed was at the Hall Farm Yard, adjacent to two pig sties, where the brick building shared a common back wall with the sheep washing dip and thus provided a good drainage pit for the waste water. The loose fitting pan tiled roof gave an easy escape for the clouds of steam that emanated from the large copper boiling away at the back of the building. Preparations began the previous evening when the brick floor was swilled down with copious quantities of water and brushed until the dark red floor bricks glistened. The pig slaughtering day generally commenced around 5 am when a coal fire was lit in the grate under the copper, that earlier had been filled with 25 gallons of water. Boards were placed over the wide copper top to support thick hessian sacks that reduced heat loss, and helped to maintain the temperature of the boiling water.

Arthur Benton from Saltfleetby who in addition to killing pigs during the winter, operated a sheep clipping gang during the early summer in addition to scything the reeds from the marsh drains for the remainder of the summer and autumn.

201

At precisely 7am the sound of tyres crunching on gravel accompanied by a rasping cough heralded Arthur's arrival by bicycle from Saltfleetby. Wearing a flat cap and old gabardine raincoat tied securely around his waist with a length of binder twine, Arthur would exchange a few pleasantries between further bouts of coughing, no doubt exacerbated by his bike journey in the cold morning air. He started to prepare himself for work by untying the twine and removing his coat, and then opening a neatly tied hessian bag from the rear carrier of his cycle where he extracted a carefully folded brown workshop coat along with his knives and other tools for dressing the carcase. Arthur was a man of few words particularly at this time of day, as perhaps a consequence of his cigarettes he would give a few more wheezy coughs, and then carefully roll another cigarette as he busied himself sharpening knives and generally getting the tools that he was going to use in the correct order. The water was now boiling furiously as the first glimmers of light started to etch their way across a wintry sky and began to illuminate other buildings in the farmyard. Lighting a matchstick thick cigarette and adjusting it firmly in the corner of his mouth, Arthur, would announce purposefully, "Are yer ready?"

I always had mixed emotions on pig killing days, as the couple of pigs in the next door shed that were shortly to be killed had been born on the farm many months earlier, when I had excitedly discovered one morning that their mother had farrowed, and with keen anticipation had counted all the pink skinned tiny piglets. The small pigs alternated between basking under an infrared heat lamp suspended above a fenced off corner of the building which was designed to prevent the sow crushing them as she laid down, and suckling at the milk bar. Their enormous mother continually gave the piglets reassuring grunts as she lay completely flat on a bed of clean straw.

After eight weeks the piglets were weaned having grown rapidly from their initial birth weight of about two kilos to around twenty kilos. In due course their brothers and sisters were sold when they attained approximately 70 Kgs in weight, whilst the two retained would have the sty to themselves as they led a life of riley for most of the next year, only needing to eat and sleep. I recognized of course that these animals had had a comfortable life here and that the purpose of keeping farm animals is to provide food for us human beings.

"Owd the door", Arthur remarked opening the adjoining door then without any further preamble added, "which one du yer want fost",

Replying "It doesn't matter," he would quickly slip a noose of strong rope around one of the pigs upper jaw. By the judicious use of sight boards the squealing animal was coaxed next door were Arthur quickly dispatched it firing a captive bolt gun against the animal's forehead. I always found this to be disturbing, trying to equate the contented creature of just a few minutes previous with the carcase that now lay before me. However the death had been incredibly quick and the process of preparing the carcase could now commence.

Swiftly the pig was pulled up vertical, by a set of pulleys with one end of the pulleys anchored to the building's roof and the other end attached to the animals back legs in order that Arthur could cut the pig's throat so that all the animals' blood would completely drain from the carcass. As the last drops of rapidly coagulating blood were swilled off the floor, to vanish through the drain hole in the wall into the now reddening pool beyond, the pig's carcase was lowered, to lie horizontally on to the Cratch. *(a low slatted table with carrying handles placed at either end, that rather resembled the type of handles found on a 17th century sedan).*

Readjusting his now extinguished cigarette to the corner of his mouth, Arthur, pushing his cap further up his forehead would remark in a commanding manner, "We' ell eve some watter now." As copious quantities of scalding hot water were slowly ladled over the pigs skin he used a special tool that resembled a very much strengthened small metal saucepan lid with the sharp edge down, with quick sideway movements of the tool he would dexterously extract the now loosened bristles. When all the bristles had been removed, the pulley ropes were heaved once again to raise the pig by its back legs into a vertical position.

With a nonchalance achieved by years of repetition Arthur carefully rolled another cigarette, then giving his cap a slight tug carefully extracted a short pointed knife and a rub stone from his bag of tools, and proceed with an ease achieved by years of practice to rhythmically pass the sharpening stone either side of the knife until it was razor sharp. His next task was to remove the intestines, so he made an incision between the animals back legs, and carefully inserted the index finger of his other hand pulling the loose skin away from internal organs as he swiftly drew the knife down. Expelling a myriad array of pale blue bulbous steaming intestines onto the Cratch, he announced, "Ev yer got a bucket?". He then deftly extracted the heart from the lungs and cut away the large plaice shaped liver depositing both into a galvanised metal bucket. He then set about disentangling great lengths of small intestine, to be used for sausage skins from the white fat contoured clear membrane, (called apron which would be used for covering haslets), which he cleaned by pulling the tubes between his thumb and forefinger propelling the paste coloured contents into another bucket. Arthur then looked inside the carcase and with a few sharp flicks of his knife removed the large lengths of snow white fat that encircled the two kidneys, quickly followed by removing the two lean meated fillets.

Heart, liver, kidney, fillet and apron were quickly transported home to mother who would arrange a selection of the "pigs fry" meats on dinner plates, covering them with "apron" for distribution to friends and relatives.

Exactly the same procedure was carried out with the other pig as generally two were killed at the same time.

"I'll be ere in the mornin at 8 to cut up" Arthur would chestily announce as lighting another cigarette he would mount his cycle for his return journey back to Saltfleetby.

The next morning he generally arrived a little later to butcher the now stone cold carcase using an assortment of knives plus a meat saw and cleaver. He started by sawing two parallel cuts, each about three inches from the centre of the animals back that continued down the full length of the carcase from tail to head exposing a six inch strip of meat called the chine. *"Ow do yer want um"*, he would ask, referring to the size of the chine's. *"Cut two large ones at the shoulder end for salting, (the salted chine's were stuffed with the first crop of parsley in May to make the famous Lincolnshire delicacy of stuffed chine), and the others going down to the tail can cut be smaller as we shall use them as pork"*.

Stuffed chine is a Lincolnshire speciality dish that is prepared from a salted pig's chine, and preferably from a very big pig, that is sliced whilst raw with a series of five millimetre slits extending from the back bone to the skin, with the resultant slits stuffed with finely minced parsley. After stuffing the chine is wrapped in a cloth and boiled slowly for four hours. When cold it is served in slices that are cut at right angles to the parsley stuffing. This is then sprinkled with vinegar and freshly prepared Colmans mustard to create the unique taste that Lincolnshire folk crave, and to which new converts rapidly become addicted.

Each side of the pig yields a large ham from the animals back end, a middle section of very fat meat called the flitch from the pigs belly and finally the shoulder from the head end. As the large joints of meat were cut up Arthur trimed off surplus meat to be used for sausage making and cut off the ends of the exposed knuckle bones in order that the meat will more easily take salt for the curing process.

After collecting his fee and lighting another cigarette, Arthur would remount his cycle and with a parting wave of the hand say cheerily over his shoulder, "See yer at clippin", referring to his sheep shearing work in the spring.

The various sections of meat were transported to the farmhouse in order that the business of putting away the pig could commence. A copper nailed six by four foot wooden salting tub would previously have been brought out of storage, and following a thorough washing be positioned in an outhouse. A liberal layer of coarse salt was applied to the inside of the tub. The six, large sections of meat and the chine for salting were then placed in the trough first with each piece receiving a liberal rubbing of salt, especially into the thicker parts of the hams and shoulders in order that they could cure properly. The rest of the meat and fat was now dealt with under mother's supervision in the kitchen, creating one of the rare occasions when we entered her domain. "Now Brian" she would remark to my father, "put the apron over your head and tie the strings securely behind your back, - and mind you don't drop any fat onto the floor, - oh and spread that newspaper further over so that it will catch anything else that drops". It was very much a feature of those times, and certainly the case in our household that whilst the menfolk worked outside, everything inside the house was the total domain of the wife, and in this case my mother, but at pig killing she required additional help inside the house.

Putting away a pig involved quite a lot of hard physical work, in particular turning the handle of the big stainless steel mincing machine that was retrieved from the top shelf of the pantry, and securely fastened onto the side of the substantial kitchen table. My father and I took it in turns to operate the back aching chore of turning the mincer handle with one hand, whilst using the other hand to press lumps of meat into the machines throat. The first operation involved cutting the fat into small pieces of a suitable size that could be more easily fed into the mincing machine where it was finely chopped so that as it exited through the multi holed back plate it rather resembled a seething mass of white worms. The minced fat was then transferred into a large saucepan and boiled for three hours during which time it was constantly stirred to prevent it sticking to the pans base and burning. On completion of the boiling process it was strained through a fine muslin cloth and poured into metal containers where after several hours it set hard into pure white lard.

The best and purest lard comes from the fat that encircles the kidneys whilst the fat that comes from meat trimmings does not have the same purity and consequently is the first to be used for baking and cooking.

After the fat had been minced, attention turned to sausage making. Yards of pigs intestines would have come into the house the previous day to provide the skins for the sausages, when mother scraped them clean with a wooden spoon as she turned them inside out and scraped them once again before placing them in a bowl of brine overnight.

I remember that when I first saw the contents that were being ejected I was repulsed at the thought of eating them filled with sausage meat.

The lumps of lean meat, that Arthur had pared from the inside of hams and shoulders intended for salting, were cut into smaller pieces and put through the mincer in the same way that the fat had been minced earlier before being deposited into a large enamelled container. Mother then added stale bread (that had had the crusts removed and had been soaked in water overnight) followed by the addition of generous amounts of chopped sage, salt and pepper to give them the unique Lincolnshire flavour. Strangely quantities were never measured so that uniquely no two batches of sausages ever tasted quite the same. All the ingredients were thoroughly mixed together and then put through the mincer a second time using a slightly finer cutting mechanism, followed by a further bout of mixing and test frying. After the addition of more seasoning, and further test frying mother would at last declare the sausages satisfactory, and we could commence the process of filling the sausage skins.

All that remained was for the sausage meat to be fed through the mincer once again, this time minus the cutting disc, but with the addition of a long chimney like attachment, over which the sausage skins are stretched and filled. Finally the lengths were twisted into links of eight to ten sausages. Those that were not consumed immediately were hung from bacon hooks fastened to the kitchen ceiling to dry as a form of preservative, when they would be used over the ensuing months. As time went by these dried sausages developed a more intense flavour as the meats turned slightly sour which wasn't to everyone's liking as it became an acquired taste.

After six weeks curing the salted meat was removed from the salting trough and thoroughly washed with cold water in order to remove any surface salt. When the water had drained off one end of a double pointed hook was forced through the now tough skin of the hams, shoulders, flitches and chine's, which were hung on hooks alongside the sausages.

Six weeks later the now completely dry meat was tightly bagged in white pillowcase like bags to prevent the ingression of flies. Much later before the cured meat was eaten it had to be soaked in water overnight to dissipate some of the salt. The fat flitch bacon which came from the pigs belly had the merest streak of lean running through a sea of fat and consequently wasn't a dish for those who cut fat off their meat.

Many farm workers of 50 years ago, would sit under a hedge bottom eating their pack up consisting of a slice of flitch bacon between two slices of bread and a raw shallot onion washed down with a bottle of sweetened, milkless cold tea. In our twenty first century sanitized society the techniques of slaughtering and preserving pig meat that effectively ended 40 years ago are now abhorred for fear of catching a multitude of illnesses, yet nobody in those days seemed to suffer any ill effects. Very occasionally despite the best efforts of rubbing salt into the meat, some of it, and invariably a ham because it has a much greater thickness of meat for the salt to penetrate wouldn't take salt properly. Parts of the flesh acquired an extremely strong smell that could be likened to the very worst smelling cheese, rendering it completely inedible for the vast majority of people, but I remember that our chimney sweep of 50 years ago quite enjoyed the flavour.

As the sun sinks lower in the sky and shadows lengthen I can just detect the first grey wisps of evening mist rising from the shaded edge of a grass field lying beyond an overgrown hawthorn hedge. It heralds the onset of a cooler evening, whilst beyond the grass field smoke rises from a cottage chimney which reminds me of Harry Smith, our local chimney sweep.

He used to pay my mother a visit every May to sweep the house chimneys, when she no longer required a fire in the living room, although she still had a fire in the kitchen range to provide hot water and heat for cooking in the side oven. She was always apprehensive about Harrys visit, regarding it as a necessary evil; as she feared that grains of black greasy soot would inevitable get in to some part of the house. Harry was a Mr Pickwick type character whose round smiling face peered through a pair of wire framed glasses with thick round lenses and hooks that disappeared beneath his sooty flat cap, while his black trousers fitted snugly under a loose fitting black washable cotton jacket.

Extracting himself from behind the wheel of his dark blue three wheeled Reliant Robin car with the black bristles of his brush cheekily peering out the top of his bag of rods, as if impatient to be exploring hidden soot deposits, he would hesitantly walk to the back door of our house, no doubt recalling from previous years my mother's concerns about soot getting on to her carpets. *"Now you will be careful that you don't drop any soot on my beige carpet"*, mother would chide as Harry unfurled an ominously black coloured sheet in front of the hearth. *"No Missus yer woant even know Ive been when Ive gone"*, he would reply in a high pitched squeaky voice. I'm not convinced that mother saw it that way, as she commenced a campaign of cleaning that would take some weeks to run its course before she could entirely eliminate soot from her cleaning schedule. *"Now young man"*, he would say to me, *"I want yer to go outside an gi me a shout when it's out"*, Within a few minutes I would hear muffled scraping sounds as Harry added more rods to extend the brush further up the chimney. Suddenly with a shower of soot the brush would bounce out the chimney pot, but as the bristles sprang back to their original shape very fine soot particles settled over the house down below. They landed not only on the cream painted window sills but deposited a light film over the path leading up to the back door, ready to be picked up on the shoe soles of the next person to enter the house. As Harry unscrewed the rods and retraced the brush, particles of fine soot, looking rather like puffs of black smoke escaped from behind the sheet that he had placed over the fireplace covering the hearth.. With a satisfied air of a job well done Harry would step up from a kneeling position by the fire, then with a broad grin spreading over his soot blackened face give my mother his usual remark. *"It'll draw well naw missus"*, as he bent down and picked up a bucketful of soot which he carried to the bottom of the garden and deposited on top of our soot heap, Father used to put a little soot around the stems of tender garden plants to prevent slugs and snails devouring them as slugs and snails are deterred by crossing a sooty barrier.

During the Second World War at a time when meat was still strictly rationed, farmers and other country folk had a special dispensation to slaughter pigs, provided that the meat was solely for their own consumption. Severe financial penalties leading to imprisonment were imposed if it came to the authority's attention that the rules had been flouted, so one day after Harry had swept the chimneys he looked furtively around him when he saw my father approaching, then sweeping the last of the soot from the hearth into a bucket beckoned my father over and said in a conspiratorial hushed tone,

"Ev yer got eny bacon thets gone off an yer gone r chuck away, hey I do like it wen its got a bit o' flavour". I wonder if working among soot had altered his stomach's constitution in such a manner that he could tolerate food that most people would find repugnant.

CHAPTER 19
On the Mains

As my eyes lazily sweep over the surrounding countryside, my senses are jarred into twenty first century reality by the line of high voltage electricity poles marching in an easterly direction across the northern slope of Conscience Hill.

During my lifetime, I have seen a network of poles supporting the wires that convey the invisible genie of electricity, radiate like strands of mushroom mycelium to isolated farms and remote houses throughout the marsh, where it has completely transformed the lives of the folk who live there.

I clearly remember the feeling of elation in the village, following a long period of anticipation, when on a memorable day in late summer 1947 the smoky paraffin lamps were finally relegated to a dusty outhouse shelf as the magic of the electric light became a reality. Today we take electricity completely for granted, and think nothing of the ability to plug an appliance into the mains socket confident that it will supply the power to provide heat and light as it unhesitatingly undertakes any task effortlessly, giving us more leisure time to view the world from our armchair. Prior to 1947 this was a pipe dream to residents of South Cockerington who like the majority of country dwellers loathed the onset of dark winter nights having to rely on flickering candles or smoky oil lamps to give them illumination.

With no electric cooker or immersion heater to call upon everyone depended on either a paraffin stove for cooking, or the more usual combination of fireside range that provided heat for cooking in a side oven and hot water from the back boiler, when woe betide anyone who ran out of coal, or failed to keep their two gallon paraffin can topped up. Those lucky enough to travel to Louth could get their accumulator recharged and listen to a radio; otherwise the principle evening recreation during the long winter months was reading, but always being careful not to obscure the meagre lamplight from others who were also reading.

As there was no such thing as central heating in our homes at that time it was little wonder that on many occasions during the winter months

I went to bed glimpsing a distorted moon's reflection battling with elaborate ice ferns on the bedroom window pane. Unlike many other villages that received mains electricity via overhead poles during the 1960s, South Cockerington was quite fortunate as it received its supply much earlier by an extension of the underground cable that fed electricity to Grimoldby from the next door important RAF base at Manby. I clearly remember the furious activity during the hot summers of 1947 and 1948, as trenching machines chewed through the soil to bury the smoky grey coloured electricity cable around the village, followed by frenetic activity as houses and farms were wired up.

At the rear of South View Farmyard an abandoned grooms hut had become a dejected looking relic of the horse era, and was slowly decaying amidst a sea of rampant nettles. It was resurrected as the living quarters for Mr. Johnson and two other workmen from Nottingham who were specially hired to spend several months installing electric wiring in all the farms houses and buildings. Coils of pink, fabric covered wire lay amidst innumerable lengths of bright metal conduit piping, switch gears, junction boxes and cabling. It all looked riveting stuff to children of my age, though the clouds of fine grey dust erupting from Mr Johnson and his men chopping channels in the plaster walls of the house for cables and plugs dismayed mother. Eventually the operation was completed and the eagerly awaited switch on occurred, when at a stroke, our lives were revolutionised as it removed the repetitive drudgery of oil lamps and a great deal of hand labour, enabling my mother's life particularly to change radically for the better.

In spite of post-war shortages she was able to purchase a Revo electric cooker from the Yorkshire Electricity Board, which gave her unfailing service for the next fifty years rendering the oven in the kitchen range redundant.

Previously clothes' washing was carried out every Monday morning by Mrs Vickers whose husband Moses worked on the farm. The copper in the adjoining washhouse was filled on the Sunday night, with soft water collected from the house roofs and stored in a large red painted, corrugated iron tank that stood near the house back door.

My father would light the fire under the copper before 6am to ensure that the water was boiling for Mrs. Vickers 8am arrival. Clothes were then systematically transferred to a barrel shaped dolly tub filled with boiling water from the copper and rotated with a rapid reciprocating action of the wrists using a four pronged "dolly" as clouds of steam erupted through a miasma of frothy bubbles. Mrs Vickers in common with many women of that period wore an all encompassing floral patterned pinafore around her well rounded frame, then adjusting her head scarf she would bend over the chipped brown glazed sink to rinse the last of the soap from the clothes.

The next operation involved turning the handle of the cast iron mangle as she carefully fed the washed garments through its worn wooden rollers, to the accompaniment of popping sounds, as water was ejected at high pressure causing the garments to be flattened to something resembling thin boards. When the last of the garments had been pegged out to dry on the clothes line set between poles in the paddock and were blowing nicely in the wind, Mrs Vickers returned to the kitchen where she wearily sat in a chair for a well earned cup of tea and a chat with mother.

Mothers Hotpoint washing machine purchased 1947 and still working well at the time of her death almost 67 years later.

Retrieving a camphor smelling handkerchief from within the folds of her pinny her usual remarks would be, *"Wael thets it fer anuther week Mrs Needam I wunder what next weak ull bring us"*.

She was thoroughly dependable and never missed a Monday washday, but the arrival of electricity signalled a change as mother was now able to pick a good drying day and do all the wash herself in her new Hotpoint washing machine, with its rubber mangle rollers mounted on top. It gave her unfailing service until the end of her life more than 50 years later. An Electrolux vacuum cleaner soon arrived in the house followed by a mains powered radio, that ensured we could hear Dick Barton special agent without fear of a flat accumulator.

The arrival of electricity on the farm illuminated the darkest corners of cobweb infested buildings. Electric motors opened up a wealth of labour saving solutions, eliminating for example the back breaking task of cutting Swedes with a hand turned root slicer. An electric motor coupled to the machine by a flat driving belt did the work with just a flick of a switch.

Mains electricity enabled us to commence the mechanisation of cereal production by using electric motors to operate drying systems and convey grain in bulk. It cannot be over stated that without electricity, modern farming as we know it today would be almost impossible to carry out.

Mains water came to the village about the same time as mains electricity and had a similarly profound effect on people's lives. Up to that time only the larger houses had a well but this still required the water to be pumped by hand up to a header tank, as I knew full well at Hill House, because as soon as I was big enough to operate the pump handle, this was my nightly task. Those households without a well had to carry all their water from the nearest pump which inevitably made everyone extremely careful about water usage. Twenty first century householders are far too proliferate with their water usage and could well learn a lesson from the position that existed only sixty years ago. At that time everybody had a water butt to catch rain water that fell on the house roof, which was used for clothes washing and garden watering if there was sufficient spare. Bath nights in most village households were weekly rituals that took place in a tin bath placed in front of the kitchen fire, because not only was it a warm spot, to undress but it was also the nearest point to the tap delivering hot water from the back boiler. There is little wonder therefore that the same water was used for all the family when every drop had to be carried, sometimes for a distance of 100 yards or more.

Another such inconvenience was a visit to the privy. How well I remember sitting there on a cold winters day, crumpling up a newspaper square in an effort to soften it prior to use! As there were no flush toilets all human waste was caught in wide necked buckets, sited under a board, containing two seats, (one mainly for solids and the other for liquids,) within a small brick privy building, because of the smell, particularly in the summer months it was generally sited well away from the house at the bottom of the garden. All the sewage was recycled through the vegetable garden that helped towards producing abundant crops.

The introduction of mains water had an equally profound effect on our and other livestock farms in the village, because prior to the arrival of mains water, all fields grazing stock were watered either by a water tanker, dew pond, or a ditch. The many sub divisions of Monks Dyke that passed through the village had a succession of "waterings" let into the bank where stock could drink from the water flowing past. I remember the large riveted steel tanks set on pillars a few feet above ground level adjacent to farm buildings that were designed to catch rain water falling on the roofs. Lead piping delivered water from these tanks to drinking troughs within the crew yards whilst water had to be carried by bucket into some seperate stables. The introduction of mains water led to all grass fields receiving a piped supply into a concrete trough manufactured by Skegnes cast stone. The excellence of their durability is shown by the fact that they are still giving sterling service today, over 60 years later.

Street lighting was installed along the village lanes and paths in 1968, enabling villagers to walk safely along the lanes after dark without having to carry a storm lantern or torch.

During 1972 mains sewage was installed throughout the village making a major impact on village hygiene and smells. From the time that mains water was connected to the village, folk who had installed flush toilets relied on a sceptic tank system to purify toilet waste, whilst other brown water was discharged untreated direct into Monks Dyke.

Inevitably during the summer months Monks Dyke dried up as since the introduction of mains water there was now no necessity to maintain a flow of water from the springs at Louth, but in any event post war housing to the east of Louth led to the diversion of the spring water down to the River Lud. In many ways, Monks Dyke as it passed down Chapel Lane in the village, had devolved into little more than an open sewer containing lagoons of evil smelling liquid that as the ditch dried gave it the consistency of black jelly. About this time in 1972 a dustbin collection service was inaugurated which eliminated the need for household rubbish dumps generally located adjacent to the brick privies in most gardens.

In the space of 26 years the village attained all the amenities of a town dweller, enabling it in common with villages up and down the country, to assume a new role as a dormitory village populated with a high proportion of transitory residents. The lack of village allegiance is graphically illustrated by comparing the 2001 Register of Electors with 2008, when only seven years later, out of 186 people registered to vote in the village, 84 or 45% had either died or moved on elsewhere.

CHAPTER 20
Monks Dyke and the Abbey

"The dykes dry and the beast are bealing, if we don't get water to 'em they'll break out", my father announced to my mother, with a look of exasperation on his face as he completed his regular breakfast of a boiled egg and a couple of slices of cold, fat bacon seasoned with a splash of Worcester sauce.

"Henry Parker or Green on the Louth Road must have been across Conscience Hill again and let all the water go their way".

On completing his breakfast he untied Dolly's, reins, (a large over fat pony), then with a couple of clicks of his tongue followed by "git on" he jumped into the back of the trap as Dolly cantered up Pedlar Lane to the Louth Road to the point where the branch of Monks Dyke, called Green Dyke leading to North Cockerington, passes under the road.

My father used to inspect the animals in every field around the farm on a daily basis throughout the summer months from his pony and trap, paying particular attention to the supply of water flowing down Monks Dyke.

Monks Dyke was a vital man made ditch that had been dug to convey water from a spring in Aswell Street, Louth to the Abbey at Louth Park, after which the natural fall of land carried the ditch of water eastwards for another half mile or so until the mass of Conscience Hill blocked its direct progress.

A small wooden weir spanned the ditch at the western edge of Conscience Hill, in front of a brick pier, which was designed to precisely divide the flow of water, so that exactly half went in a northerly direction to North Cockerington and half south to South Cockerington. Many disputes arose between farmers from the two villages over the fair distribution of Monks Dyke's water, because from time to time unscrupulous individuals would visit the division and undermine the bank on the North Cockerington side of the weir where the ditch level was naturally lower in order that more water could go in their direction.

The supply was also frequently interrupted alongside Monks Dyke Road in Louth as the ditch traversed a slope, with the lower bank of the ditch either being breached, sometimes maliciously, or on other occasions becoming dammed by an accumulation of debris that had been dumped in the water course, allowing the precious water to escape. If the flow downstream was either restricted or cut off farmers from both villages quickly panicked as livestock could not live long without access to water.

My father arrived at the point where the North Cockerington branch of Monks Dyke crossed the Louth Road adjacent to Mr Green's small farm, where he kept and milked half a dozen Guernsey cows. As practically all the water for watering his stock and washing down his dairy shed came from Monks Dyke, he was usually the culprit who had deprived the South Cockerington branch of its water by digging a channel into the earthen North Cockerington bank resulting in all the water going in that direction. Usually when my father challenged him he would deny all knowledge claiming "it wis Enery meester". Enery, Henry Parker lived at Crossmoor farm about 250 yards beyond Mr. Green's farm alongside Green dyke, which was the name given to the North Cockerington branch of Monks Dyke. Henry had a sallow complexion and from my experience rarely broke into a smile, his bottle was always half empty and disaster in his eyes always seemed to be imminent. Wearing his flat cap screwed half over his right ear, a loose fitting jacket and rolled down thigh boots, Henry could be found most Fridays assisting the auctioneers in the pig section at Louth market. Wielding a flat board he steered a reluctant selection of squealing pigs into their pens. When not assisting at Louth and other adjacent markets, Henry could be found in a vehicle that was mid way in size between a large pickup truck and a small lorry, transporting one of his boar pigs from farm to farm to service farmer's sows. When father politely enquired if he had any knowledge regarding changes to the equitable distribution of the water flow, Henry would defensively say, "Ive ad nowt to do we it, yer want ter tawk ter yon fella" pointing in the direction of Mr. Green's farm. The matter could never be satisfactorily resolved and always entailed my father walking alongside the ditch up to the division and spading earth into the breach thus restoring a supply of the precious water.

The ditch in 2011 showing the division with Conscience Hill to the rear.

The last crumbling remains of Louth Park Abbey.

Where Louth Abbey once stood

Remains of a wall constructed of chalk and sandstone

219

In 1132 Cistercian Monks founded an Abbey at Fountains Abbey in North Yorkshire. Four years later a group split away and founded an Abbey in Haverholme, a few miles north east of Sleaford which only two years later, they sold to the new strict monastic order of St Gilbert of Sempringham. The Bishop of Lincoln, Alexander the Magnificent, granted them lands to relocate and found a new Abbey between Louth and Cockerington, "to include the right to feed swine in the wood there and have a mill on the River Lud", which would form the northern boundary of the property.

The Cistercians developed sheep farming for both the domestic and overseas wool markets that were under the control of a merchant who acted as the middleman between the sheep grazers and the weavers, a position that exists to this day in most types of agricultural production.

The merchant who would invariably be from the Low Countries visited the monastic sheep flocks in spring in order to determine how much wool was likely to be shorn, and after negotiating a price would organise transport for the wool through the local port at Saltfleet, which luckily for the Abbey's continuing trade was one of the country's leading ports in the 14 and 15th century's. Within thirty years the production of wool was so successful that the Louth Park Abbot was able to conclude a six year contract with a Flemish merchant to supply wool. Although the number of monks at the Abbey would rarely exceed one hundred, they controlled a large number of illiterate lay brothers called Conversi, who did the majority of the manual work, such as digging the channel or dyke from the St. Helen and Aswell Springs in Louth to supply water to the Abbey that they were constructing two miles east of Louth. The ditch that encircled the Abbey created a 23 acre island as it passed through two sizable ponds,t providing fish for the Monks. It was salted in order that it could be preserved, to supplement their monotonous diet of Horsebread, oat gruel and very occasionally mutton. Horsebread was a very coarse dry bread made from grains of wheat, barley and oats, that was usually served hard and stale and accompanied by weak ale to drink.

The extensive grounds contained the principle buildings, along with gardens and orchards in addition to a vineyard enabling them to produce their own wine. The vast 256 foot long Abbey, which was 71 feet longer than the nearby parish church of St. James in Louth was almost as wide as Lincoln Cathedral. The Abbey would have looked an imposing feature on the South Cockerington village skyline, and must have completely dominated the view from my position on Conscience Hill less than a mile away. It was constructed of hard grey Ancaster limestone, interspersed with the much softer Spilsby green sandstone which was also used for South Cockerington church, whilst other parts of the building were constructed of locally excavated soft white chalk. In contrast the vast roof was covered with lead sheeting, except for the Chapter house that was tiled. The fortunes of the Abbey were closely linked to the adjacent lands in South Cockerington with many recorded references confirming the close inter relationship. It is of little surprise to find that after a short period of time the Abbey lands were extended when Abbot Dunham purchased 40 acres of woodland from the Vavasours who owned the Cockerington lands. In 1341, the Abbot resorted to law to graze sheep on 1000 acres of common land in Cockerington after the harvest was taken. The next year the Abbot petitioned the Pope requesting that the papal taxes be reduced as there had been a succession of very poor harvests leaving the Abbey in deep debt.

In 1342 Sir Henry le Vavasour the lord of the manor in South Cockerington was taken gravely ill and his doctor thought that his chances of recovery would improve if he were moved to the Abbey. From my position here I can clearly see the route that the terminally ill knight would have taken as he was transported the two miles from his home in South Cockerington to the Abbey. It doesn't require too much imagination to visualize a wooden wheeled cart, probably pulled by two oxen, lurching from side to side as it traversed the length of Stewton Road's rough track. It was believed in those days, if monies were bequeathed to religious institutions the monks would pray for the deceased and so assist the soul's passage into the next world. So it was, Sir Henry recognising his position, called his lawyer to draw up a document which would provide funding for the monks to pray for him. The Abbot skillfully arranged for the dying man to sign another document, assigning all the manorial estates over to the Abbey, (to the astonishment of Sir Henry's wife and family), when perhaps with more than a pang of "conscience" he decreed that Sir Henry's body should be buried in a privileged position alongside past Abbots under the great altar in the Abbey. Sir Henrys widow, Lady Constance was outraged at the devious actions of the Abbot, accusing him of forging the document whereupon the wily Abbot countered by accusing her of being complicit in stealing the title and deeds relating to various lands. The dispute went to the court of King Edward 111rd, where Lady Constance claimed that the charter had been fabricated after Sir Henry's death, this resulted in Walter of Louth, the Abbot of Louth

Park Abbey standing trial as to whether he had fairly obtained the Manor of Cockerington for the Abbey.

In those times Abbots and Priors, wielded great power with many of them owing their appointment to currying favour with either the monarch or one of his supporting Earls. Much depended on being on the right side, so it would appear that Abbot Walter was in the King's favour because he satisfied the court and was allowed to keep the Manor, provided he paid rent to the widow and her heirs. Later there was a compromise that allowed the Vavasour family to regain the Manor house, but left ownership of the Cockerington lands with the Abbey. Four years later the Abbey was struck by Bubonic Plague commonly known as the Black Death and recorded by the Louth Park Chronicle in the following terms. *"In this year many monks of Louth Park died amongst them died Walter of Louth, Lord Abbot,on the 3rd of July 1349, who suffered very great persecution on account of the Manor of Cockerington and was buried before the great altar near Sir Henry Vavasour, Knight."* It goes on to record, *"the scourge annihilated at once the confessor and the penitent"*.

Could this I wonder offer a connection to Conscience Hill? *"This scourge in many places left less than a fifth of the population surviving. A deadly blow struck by the omnipotent hand of God, sweeping away a greater multitude than that destroyed in the day of Noah."*

The death toll arising from the plague had a devastating effect on the Abbey, resulting in substantial falls in income probably due to poor farming practices. This was exacerbated by a drop in the price of wool and land being leased off to tenant farmers at poor rents leaving the Abbey responsible for repairs which further contributed to the loss of income. Another item in the Chronicle lists under repairs,

12 shillings and six pence on Richard Reynolds farm at Cockerington." This was a significant sum at that time, when many labourers worked a 12 hour day for 1d.

When Henry V111th dissolved the Abbey, 1535-1536, there were then only ten monks under Abbot George Walker. At the dissolution, all of the vestments, lead and plate went to the King, when it was said that the 'value of the lead and bells amounted to £598 13 shillings'. Much of the stone was carted to Louth for the construction of a new market house and street paving at Aswell Street spring.

As I record the devious exploits involved by Abbot Walter in stealing the Cockerington Manor Estate from Lady Constance, it's possible to hypothesise on why Conscience Hill acquired its name. I believe it highly likely that Abbot Walter's devious actions when he is referred to as confessor would have played on his conscience to such a degree that his sharp practice must have disturbed him.

Is it possible, I muse sitting here that he would have felt utterly ashamed of his devious actions resulting in him retreating from the precincts of the Abbey to this nearby high spot to seek forgiveness from his maker for such a dishonest deed. The monks under his authority would witness this act of contrition, and consequently gave the nearby hill the name that has endured to this day, - Conscience Hill.

Every field that fronted onto Monks Dyke had what was termed as a "watering". It comprised an approximate, 20 foot wide, slope leading from the field down to the water in the ditch. A retaining board was placed at the water's edge to prevent animal's stepping into the ditch itself and fouling the water. The sides of the slope were fenced and the slope was lined with locally produced chalk from a nearby Wolds quarry to prevent it becoming a muddy swamp. These 'waterings' were the sole means of providing drinking water for stock so it was vital that the supply from Louth was maintained.

As Monks Dyke leaves Conscience Hill on the South Cockerington side it divides once again, with one part going towards Chapel Lane in the village and the other diverted to feed water to South View Farm and The Hall complex. Where Monks Dyke joined the corner of Pedlar and Southview Lane, at a point later named Ram corner, because a hydraulic ram was constructed there. It used a proportion of the water flow to power an hydraulic pump which raised a much smaller volume to a tank about 12 feet above ground level. The tank provided a low pressure piped system supplying water to both South View Farmyard and Hill House Farm.

The water was split once more at Ram corner with another section of the ditch conveying water to Hall Farm, providing water for the various moats around the farmyard, and subsequently to moats around The Hall itself before finally discharging into a series of stocked fishponds.

At Hall Farm it passed through a tunnel before flowing into a brick lined pit approximately 12 feet square and 4 feet deep, known as the Washdyke. Sheep were washed there in cold water, in order to disperse the natural lanolin in the sheep's fleece prior to shearing. My father used to 'dip' the sheep by standing within a wooden barrel in the centre of the pool using a long wooden handle with a T shaped curved piece of wood on the end called a 'poi'.

The sheep were lowered into the water on their backs in order that water could more easily penetrate the fleece of the inverted animals and so disperse the grease, soil and dust debris that had accumulated in the fleece over the year. My father's task was to submerge the sheep a few more times by means of the poi in order that the fleece was completely saturated. Sheep washing was carried out towards the end of May about a couple of weeks before the sheep were clipped.

Before the annual sheep washing could take place the washing pit had to be cleaned out, not only from the muck accruing from washing the previous year's dirty fleeces, but also from leaves and other debris that had blown in over the year. I'm not entirely sure if eels fed on the accumulated muck but the pit teemed with eels providing one of the farms seasonal delicacies. The slippery eels were skinned and then chopped into one inch lengths, cooked and served in a well seasoned, creamy sauce liberally mixed with new season's parsley.

This seasonal offering was closely followed by two other traditional spring dishes, Rook pie and Stuffed Chine. Warm early evenings towards the end of May encouraged young rooks to fly when they were relatively easy to shoot, though difficult to spot amidst the lush green canopy of the horse chestnut trees. There were then, and still are, large numbers of rooks which constitute a serious farm pest devouring spring sown grain crops and decimating crops at harvest time. The young rooks were skinned and the breasts baked in a crusted pie that was served heavily seasoned with the first new potatoes, a delicious dish!

The Black Death that killed Walter the Lord Abbot of Louth Park Abbey in 1349 was a devastating disease which also killed 80 % of the population of Lincolnshire between early 1349 and 1350.

It is believed that the disease originated in Mongolia and then following trade routes spread to China between 1330 and 1333, when it was carried by traders conveying spices and other oriental goods from the Far East to southern Europe. The highly contagious infection arrived by ship in the south west of England in midsummer 1348 and spread rapidly across the country covering the 400 miles to Lincolnshire in less than six months, and that was in spite of a very small population in the country who rarely travelled very far. The plague was transmitted by fleas carried by black rats and then transferred between people by human fleas and even spread on breath from person to person. The name Black Death was derived from the multitude of black spots caused by the bacillus Pasteurella Pestis infection arising from boil like skin eruptions that were initially to be found in soft tissue under the arms or in the groin and then spread all over the body. The illness developed rapidly from initial sneezing, followed by an unquenchable thirst and bleeding from all of the body's orifices. Very few people who contracted the disease survived as the highly infectious plague wiped out entire families and decimated the populations of towns and villages.

There are many recorded instances of Lincolnshire folk remedies using moulds to kill bacteria, from as early as the sixteenth century that predate Alexander Flemings discovery of penicillin in the 1920s. The moulds that appeared on the fat of bacon as it dried on the kitchen bacon hooks was smeared on to cuts and was said to rapidly assist the healing process. Other remedies relate to the use of mouldy bread, when it would be made into a paste and applied to the injured part of the body. Sadly there are no records of moulds being used at the time of the Black Death in Britain or there could possibly have been a different outcome as history records the Chinese using mouldy grain to treat infectious burns and wounds before the birth of Christ.

Traditional remedies abound of which some are little better than old wives tales. Until quite recently many farm workers would supplement a sandwich of fat bacon with a raw shallot, and claim that they never suffered from either a cold or the flu in spite of working extremely long hours. Often they would work in clothing that at the best was damp and the worst wet through but they rarely missed a day's work through ill health.

CHAPTER 21
The Scropes of Cockerington

Surveying the landscape displayed before me I am reminded of the Scropes and the Vavasours before them, who in earlier centuries would have owned much of the land that I can now see.

During the time that the Abbey was flourishing the Vavasours of Cockerington were a family to be reckoned with, as decisions that they made could quite literally make all the difference between life and death for the men and women who eked out a subsistence living working on their very small farms.

It doesn't require too much imagination for me to visualise a twist of smoke rising from the chimneys of a great many tiny mud and stud thatched houses stretching away into the distance. I can almost see a few hens dusting themselves in the dry earth of the farm yard, close to the house back doors, whilst a couple of cows graze in a small paddock nearby.

In the summer of 1565 Ralph Scrope of Hambelton who already owned land in other parts of the country, might well have reined in his horse on this the highest spot in the district to view his new estate.

He had just paid Sir William Vavasour £1600 for the grand Cockerington Manor and the estate that comprised much of the land that now lay before him.

Following his purchase little would alter for their many tenants in the years that lay ahead until the time of the civil war when his grandson would raise a local force from amongst their number to fight Cromwell's army at Edgehill.

Many of the features visible, to me now, would have been there 450 years ago, such as the stone church towers dotted across the marsh with many of the clumps of trees appearing pretty well unchanged as to how they look today.

The Scrope family would continuously own these lands until the Estate sold the property to Mr Wilkinson in 1920 who promptly resold it to the existing tenants, thus finally ending the landlord tenant relationship.

Sir Adrian Scropes effigy in St Edward's Church, South Cockerington.

Ralph's eldest son Adrian was born in February 1562 and was aged 20 when he married Ursula daughter of Sir John Clifton from Barrington in Somerset.

Adrian was clearly a very important figure because in 1603 he was knighted by James 1 very shortly after his accession to the throne and is described on his tomb as being thrice noble.

So highly was he regarded that following his death in 1623 a lifelike effigy was erected over his tomb in South Cockerington church. The work is attributed to Epiphanius Evesham 1570 -1633 who was a highly regarded English sculptor. There are many examples of his work throughout the country. Sir Adrian's figure is carved in white alabaster and displays him reclining with his left elbow resting upon a cushion whilst his right arm is pressed over his heart. He is dressed as a fully armed knight with close cropped hair. His facial features are exquisitely carved showing a prominent nose and strong chin.

A wide plaited collar falls to his breastplate and the sash which passes over the right shoulder and under the left arm still bears traces of the blue with which it was once painted. His feet rest against the five feathers issuing out of a crown of the Scrope crest.

His sword and gauntlets lie beside him and his helmet with closed visor stands behind his right shoulder. There are carved panels below,

Sir Gervase Scrope. From the original by kind permission of Mr and Mrs P Scrope.

one with six male figures, two of them kneeling. Over their heads is a scroll bearing the words "Similis in prole resurgo". On the other panel are two female figures kneeling, both with flowing veils from their coifs and in the far corner is an infant, in its swaddling clothes (this is probably the Ursula Scrope who died young and is buried at Berkhamptstead near Hemel Hemstead in Hertfordshire). Over these figures is a scroll engraved with "Pares et impares".

At the foot of Sir Adrians tomb, is a black marble tablet, on which is cut the following epitaph;

"Thrice noble Sir Adrian Scrope, Knight deceased December ye 10 1623.

Tombs are but Dumbe.

Lay books, they onlye keep

Their names alive, who in their wombs do sleepe;

But who would pen the virtue of this Knight

A story (not an epitaph) must write.

On his death in 1623 Sir Adrian was succeeded by his eldest son Gervase who added to the estates already considerable property in Lincolnshire by purchasing more land including 170 acres of the freshly reclaimed Porters Marsh in North Somercotes which The Environment Agency are now in 2011 proposing to return to the sea, such is progress!

Gervase was knighted by Charles I in 1630 and in 1634 he was appointed High Sherriff of Lincolnshire.

In spite of being a Royalist, he was soon in conflict with the crown over the momentous constitutional issue of Ship-money, when he protested about the unfairness of the tax. The menacing speeches that he made to the collecting officer caused him to be arrested and committed to Fleet prison in 1637.

By agreeing to plead guilty and apologise for making an objection, he was released from prison, but had to pay a fine of £50 and pay all the ship money for 1637 and 1638.

In spite of the above, he remained a loyal Royalist as he joined the Royal Standard along with his son Adrian, when civil strife began to erupt.

Clarendon in his history of the Rebellion, describes Sir Gervase as "(an old gentleman of great fortune in Lincolnshire, who raised a foot company among his tenants and brought them into the Earl of Lindseys Regiment); and being at the battle of Edgehill with his son Adrian on October 2nd 1642, he was fighting near that General, when he was taken. Sir Gervase himself fell in the strife, covered with wounds; one writer says 16, another 26 wounds". Clarendon goes on to relate "that he lay on the field stripped among the dead, from about 3pm on the afternoon of Sunday, all that cold night, all Monday, until Tuesday evening, for it was late before his young son, Mr Scrope, found him, whom, with great piety, he carried to a warm lodging and afterwards to Oxford, where he wonderfully recovered".

Considering that he lay naked for more than two days after been given up for dead, when he must have lost a great deal of blood and then been jolted incessantly on the long journey to Oxford, it speaks volumes for his resilience.

It's a remarkable testament to Gervases loyalty to the crown, that despite the severity of wounds that would almost certainly have killed a lesser man, he not only survived his ordeal but was soon in action once more.

A contemporary painting shows him with pale looking features and his left arm partly obscured by a blue scarf which is almost certainly supporting an injury to the arm.

Fuller repeats the same story, recording him among the "Worthies of Lincolnshire", adding that Sir Gervase "lived more than 10 years after, monument of God's mercy and his son's affection". He adds that "he ever after bore his arm in a scarf and loss of blood made him look very pale, as a messenger come from the grave to advise the living to prepare for death.

Allen in his history of Lincolnshire, says that Harvey (the celebrated Sir William Harvey who discovered the principles of blood circulation and the function of the heart), was physician to the king at Edgehill, when he personally attended Sir Gervase. He said that "Sir Gervase owed his life to his being stript"; he says "it was cold clear weather and a frost that night, which staunched his bleeding and about midnight, or some hours after his hurt, he awakened and was fain to drawe a dead body upon him for warmth sake".

Although not fully recovered from his ordeal Sir Gervase formed one of the garrisons at Newark until he had to surrender, when his men were allowed to lay down their arms without further bloodshed.

Now finding that he was on the losing side it was little surprise that the Parliamentarians under Cromwell should confiscate all of Sir Gervases estates in 1643, with Lady Scrope only being allowed one fifth of what the Commonwealth received by way of rents from her husband's property.

After much wrangling, in 1645 Lady Scrope was able to live in the Manor house and rent the estate from the Commonwealth, however there seems to have been many complaints about non payment of her allowance.

Sir Gervase and his son Adrian after fighting for the defeated Charles 1 had to pay Parliament several thousands of pounds by way of fines and that having done so the Government agreed that their estate "shall be henceforth clearly freed and discharged from sequestration". However they had to borrow heavily in order to pay off their fines. It is reported that their debts amounted to more than £7700.

In spite of these financial penalties, by 1653 Sir Gervase had settled his affairs to such an extent that he was able to add additional property to his estate at Cockerington.

Sir Gervase is buried at South Cockerington and left a lasting legacy by building alms houses for the poor of the village with an annual income to be paid in perpetuity.

Sir Adrian Scrope, Gervases son was born in 1615 and as mentioned previously was active like his father with the Royalist cause serving quite probably at the siege of Exeter in 1643.

Owing to the sequestration of Sir Gervase's estates and the fines which the Parliament forced upon both father and son to pay, Adrian seems to have been in a rather sorry plight.

Somewhere about 1650, we learn from the sequestration papers, that he gave an undertaking "to henceforth well and peacefully demean himself towards his Highness the Lord Protector" ; also he promised to reveal any plots that he may discover to the Major General of Lincolnshire and if he went to London he would notify his arrival within 24 hours.

It appears that only very shortly before this arrangement, an official had been ordered to apprehend young Mr Scrope of Lincolnshire, at the Blue Boar, Holborn, probably for some act prejudicial to the existing Commonwealth.

Before the Civil War was in full action, the Queen (Henrietta- Maria), had given Sir Adrian leases of land at Spalding, probably as a reward for his services at court.

Sir Gervase died in 1655 and was succeeded by his oldest son Adrian.

On becoming owner of the Cockerington estate and mansion, it appears that he preferred to live in The Close, their Lincoln mansion, on the east side of Potter Gate, which became the Episcopal residence in 1669.

But better times were at hand on the restoration of the monarchy, with the Stuarts restored to the throne once more.

Adrian was knighted in 1661 at Charles II coronation and made a knight of the Bath. He was also elected, (or awarded) along with Gervase Holles the position of MP for Grimsby a position he held until his death in 1667.

He had like his father supported the royalist cause and as he had been on the losing side incurred substantial personal debts making it impossible for him to reduce mortgages on the Cockerington Estate.

The cost of electioneering and living in London crippled his resources resulting in some of the property being mortgaged, along with his many other debts.

There is a portrait of him at Danby (the family seat in North Yorkshire) painted when he was a young man holding out his hand as if to show that he had a wound.

Sir Adrian married Mary daughter of Sir Robert Carr of Sleaford and Aswarby in about 1648. The new Queen appointed Mary to the position of first Lady in Waiting and was reported to hold her in the very highest esteem.

She along with Sir Adrian are both buried in Cockerington church.

Sir Carr Scrope who succeeded his father Sir Adrian was born at his Grandfather Carrs home at Aswarby in 1649, the year that saw the tragic death of Charles 1st.

Soon after inheriting the estate in 1667 and quite likely influenced by his mother's court connections he was created a Baronet by Charles II.

Although he never married he was described as being a literary man at the Court of Charles II, translating Virgil and Ovid in addition to his own writing.

In August 1680 accompanied by his personal physician he was in Tumbridge Wells, and "declared to be in much pain" resulting in his death later that year. He was buried in the parish of St Martin in the Field, Westminster.

His lifestyle living in London meant that he was not only unable to discharge the mortgages left by his father, but had to borrow additional money on his Mablethorpe estates and raise still further sums on other Lincolnshire property.

On his death at the age of 31 the Baronetcy of Cockerington became extinct and his younger and only brother Robert succeeded to the Cockerington estates.

Not much is known of Robert apart from the fact that he was a Catholic that cut him off from holding any official position. In 1715 he is listed as being one of the Roman Catholic Nonjurors who refused to take the oath to the King.

In spite of inheriting the estate heavily encumbered by debt, he left it almost cleared by the time of his death in 1718.

He was buried in the church of St Pancras in London, known as a place where Catholics wished to be interred.

This was a time of considerable enmity between Catholics and Protestants, which must have been exacerbated by Robert marrying Lucy Newton of Hather whose family were staunch Protestants.

Gervase Scrope, Roberts's son was born in1682 and was educated under the guardianship of his Catholic kinsmen at Danby in North Yorkshire, but unfortunately fell out of favour with his father because he decided to become a Protestant.

Gervase wrote to his uncle Sir John Newton in a letter dated January 1708, when he announced that he had made a public profession of the Protestant religion and begs Sir John to effect his reconciliation with his father.

It seems that this was done shortly before his marriage to Elizabeth Cresswell who was a protestant.

Even though he lived most of his life at The Close in Lincoln where most of his children were born, he made considerable improvements to his Cockerington estate property radically altering the old Manor House. He was largely responsible for creating the Hall that is now recognisable in photographs prior to its demolition in 1920.

He built a new Geogian facade over the old Elizabethan manor house and introduced Corinthian columns into the high ceilinged reception rooms. He built a spectacular kitchen window that contained an amazing 330 panes of glass, whilst at the back of the altered house stood an immense kitchen chimney, presumably a portion of the original house.

Gervase mentions building a bridge over the moat indicating that the original house had been partly surrounded by water. It was Gervase who was responsible for planting many of the trees around the village, many of which can still be appreciated from my Conscience Hill view point.

For the sum of £11.11 shillings he got one of his tenants to create fish ponds on some low lying ground situated 80 yards to the south of the

Hall, these were fed by water passing through a system of inter connecting moats from Monks Dyke.

He records stocking his new fish ponds with tench and carp in 1732.

Gervase records that all of the improvements that were made to the house and estate at that time cost £1742, whilst total rental income amounted to only £1500. Following his conversion to Protestantism, public positions were now open to him. In 1721 he was appointed High Sheriff of Lincolnshire, and a few years later his name is found among many other influential gentleman of the county, as one of the trustees appointed by the crown to the office of " Keepers of the Castle of Lincoln, of the gaol, and of the Shire House".

He became an acting magistrate, and from 1737 until his death was High Steward of Louth.

Gervase Scrope died in 1741 and is buried in Lincoln cathedral in between his first wife Elizabeth and second wife Frances.

Gervase had four sons, (two of whom succeeded him) and two daughters by his first wife Elizabeth and another son by Frances who also succeeded to the Cockerington estate.

Gervase the oldest son succeeded his father in 1741, but lived in the family mansion in Lincoln for the first year before he came to Cockerington.

In 1758 he took his oath of allegiance to George II when he became High Sheriff of Lincolnshire.

In 1763 he sold the mansion in Pottergate, Lincoln and moved down to Eastcolt Park, near Pinner in Middlesex where he died unmarried in 1776, but his body was brought back to Cockerington for burial.

Frederick James Scrope, his brother succeeded him but after a legal education decreed in his will that whoever inherited the estate was to bear the name of Scrope.

It is evident that Frederick had a particularly strong feeling that his roots belonged in Cockerington because he stipulated that he desired to be buried in the Scrope vault at Cockerington, as near the remains of Sir Gervase as possible.

He requested that his coffin be placed on the left side of Sir Gervase and be carried by his Lincolnshire tenants. He died in 1780 with no children.

Thomas Scrope, his half brother inherited not only the Cockerington estate but his mother Frances's estate at Coleby near Lincoln, both of which delivered a rent of £3000 per year. He lived at Coleby for most of his life becoming M P for Lincoln from 1768- 1774.

Thomas married, soon after inheriting the property, but although continuing to live at Coleby had no children.

He died in 1792 and is buried at Cockerington and so passed the last representative of his line.

Mary Scrope, the elder of Gervases two daughters married Thomas Vivian recorder of Lincoln.

Her daughter Mary Vivian, married Joshua Peat of Lincolns Inn in 1771 so that when her last remaining Scrope uncle died, she succeeded to the Cockerington property. As her uncle Frederick James had so arranged it in his will she changed their name back to Scrope.

She died without children shortly after inheriting the estate when it was then passed to William Scrope, from another branch of the family who lived at Castle Combe, near Chippenham in Wiltshire.

He died in 1852 and left the property to his daughter who married a George Thompson who also changed his name to Scrope but left no heirs.

Inheritance now passed to Thomas Scrope a cousin residing at Danby near Whitby in North Yorkshire who was responsible for replacing the original alms house by building new ones for the poor of the village, giving the occupants a weekly income of two shillings.

Upon his death in 1872 his son Major Simon Thomas Scrope inherited the estate along with all of the Scrope portraits from the extinct direct Cockerington line. He died in 1896 leaving five daughters and five sons. The eldest son Simon Conyers Scrope who never married inherited the estate but continued to live in the family home at Danby Hall.

As early as 1840 South Cockerington Hall had been rented out, when an advertisement issued by Mr Grant Allison, a Louth solicitor on July 15th 1840 elicits tenants to rent it on a yearly basis either furnished or unfurnished. The house was described as being *expensively furnished and in complete repair with a 40 feet long drawing room and a 27 feet long morning room. The dining room was a massive 30 x20 feet with 6 best bedchambers and dressing-rooms with numerous departments for servants.*

There are 2 most excellent stables, with spacious stalls for many horses and a double coach house. There is a walled garden in an excellent state of cultivation and a thriving shrubbery in front of the house with a large piece of ornamental water stocked with fish.

The advertisement goes on to describe that the Estate has gamekeepers and game on the ground that was never better than at the present time, and concludes with the statement, *"the terms will be low to an eligible tenant"*.

Kellys Lincolnshire Directory lists the Hall residents as a Mr Edward Beverly, who is described as a tenant farmer from 1872-1885 then in 1889 Mrs Fanny Beverly presumably his widow. (See Chapter 12 and the Beverley connection with Grimoldby Grange).

In 1900 Mrs Norton was living there until her death in 1908 which was followed in April 1909 by a four day sale conducted by Louth auctioneers John Taylor & Son, selling a total of 1516 lots.

As I thumb through the catalogue 100 years later I am able to gain an impression of the Halls size as it would appear that many of the contents were sold on a room by room basis.

I note that in the front kitchen an item described as – excellent dinner service of Ridgeways china, about 95 pieces realised £1 plus one shilling commission.

The oil paintings which were purchased by the late W Norton from a dispersal sale at Tong Castle in Shropshire in 1856 included a Caravegio entitled " The Death of a Virgin", -a rare gallery picture,- made 10 shillings, plus six pence commission.

Simon Conyers Scrope before his death in 1909 mortgaged some of the Cockerington estate in 1907 to provide more financial liquidity before bequeathing the property to his brother Henry Aloyius Scrope.

The now empty Hall was offered to the government during the First World War as a convalescent home for wounded soldiers and was completely refurbished by the government in 1919.

Although Mr Scrope visited the Hall from time to time someone must have born a grudge against the old gentleman because they put poison in the feed that he gave to his pheasants and partridges resulting in dead birds laying on his lawn. He was so aggrieved that he packed his bags never to return to Cockerington again.

Within months he had sold all of the Estate to Mr Wilkinson who then as mentioned earlier resold all of the property to the respective tenants.

It's not clear whether the Hall was owned by Scrope or Wilkinson when the decision was made for the building to be demolished and the resultant materials sold.

However on August 17th 1921 Messrs Nayler &Bilton sold what they described as *a valuable Small Holding of 4.3 acres being the site of South Cockerington Hall, including a modern house and a range of stabling, plus an orchard planted with fruit trees of mature growth and at present in full bearing set within an excellent walled in kitchen garden, 72x56 yards in a high state of cultivation containing about 1 acre of Potatoes included in the sale.*

There are two pumps, one in the garden, and the other adjoins the stables, both giving an excellent supply of good water.

In the grounds are two ponds or moats. The property is almost surrounded on the west and south sides by an iron fence and is eminently suited for a market gardener or cow keeper, or would form an excellent site for a gentleman's residence there being ample room for laying out a bowling green, tennis courts etc.

With the conclusion of the sale a feudal way of life which had existed for centuries between a comparative few privileged landowners with inherited lands and their tenant farmers, came to an end.

The grounds surrounding the Hall that had been a byword for excellence were starting to look quite neglected by the time of the Halls demolition in 1920.

After the reusable building materials had been cleared away all that was left was a detritus of broken bricks and plaster, as a final reminder of the grand mansion that had once stood there.

What had once been immaculately trimmed lawns and attractive, small shrubs soon sank into a wilderness of nettles, briars and elderberry bushes, leaving the larger laurels and holly bushes, that were fortunate enough to be growing beside the iron railed, perimeter fence as the sole survivors, with the last ones still visible today some 90 years later.

The brick pillars with their sandstone capping that once framed the entrance to the impressive gravel drive leading to the Halls palatial front, leaned and then finally collapsed which added to the general sense of decay as the once graceful avenue of Elms that lined its sides slowly died of old age, with the very last ones finally succumbing to the ravages of Dutch Elm disease in the 1970s.

Finally grass colonised the gravel allowing it to amalgamate with the rest of the grass in the Park field so that apart from that strip across the field having a level surface all traces of where it had once existed has disappeared.

The Hall grounds were purchased by Mr Geoffrey Thornley who used the premises and the adjoining field as a chicken farm until failing eyesight forced him to sell up in the 1960s.

Prior to Mr Thornley selling the property to Mr Arthur Whittern, who would later establish a riding school within the grounds, he felled many of the exotic trees including a magnificent specimen Turkey Oak.

Today Mr Whitterns son lives in one of two bungalows built adjacent to the site of the old Hall, whilst the stable block and coach house have been converted into another dwelling.

Cockerington Hall by kind permission of Mr and Mrs P Scrope.

CHAPTER 22
Grimoldby Grange
and the Cremery

It was while I was seeking photographs to illustrate Conscience Hill with village scenes dating back to the 1950s, that Will Hennesey of Little Carlton kindly showed me an old photograph of five figures standing in front of nearby Grimoldby Grange.

He told me that he had been given the photograph by his father in law Norman Cawkwell who had acquired it in a batch of old photographs, but neither of them could offer any explanation as to who the figures might be.

Grimoldby Grange and the 5 unidentified figures. Photo: Courtesy Mr W Hennesey

The style of their Victorian dress led me to assume that the photograph must have been taken around 1900, give or take a few years on either side of that date.

I thought that the man on the left looked very self assured, which suggested to me that he must have been a figure of considerable local importance.

It seemed more than likely that judging by his confident stance that he was the owner of Grimoldby Grange, and that the other three were his wife and children.

But just who were they?

A few days earlier by sheer coincidence Doreen Partridge nee Marriott, who now lives in North Yorkshire and had left Grimoldby in 1954, wrote a letter to the Manby and Grimoldby village news reminiscing about the happy times that she had spent in the village all those years ago.

She told me when I spoke to her recently, how she had fond memories of living with her father and mother Percy and Olive Marriott along with her two brothers at the Grange from 1945 until 1954 during the time that her father had been manager of the creamery.

We recalled how our parents used to meet from time to time for Sunday tea, an event which at the time seemed to be such a great social institution.

She included a photograph that depicted the loading dock of the Granges Co op dairy showing a lorry loaded with milk churns.

As a schoolboy I remembered the dairy which was usually referred to as the creamery, no doubt as a result of the milk being processed into butter and cheese with the whey being dried into milk powder.

Although we didn't have milk cows I vividly remember seeing churns of milk stood on wooden platforms by the gateways of many farms throughout the district.

She told me that the Co operative Wholesale Society had purchased the property from a man called Mr Harrison, but unfortunately she knew little about him or indeed any of the previous owners of Grimoldby Grange.

Although the photograph of the family was not one that I wished to use in "Conscience Hill", I was never the less curious to discover more about them, particularly as Doreen's photograph of the creamery prompted me to recall other local facilities such as the station, and other long departed village businesses that now reside only in the memories of people of a certain age.

I wanted to learn when and how the creamery came to be established at Grimoldby Grange, and perhaps discover why it closed, particularly as

Doreen's photograph showed The Grange as a hive of local industry in the early 1950s.

I regarded it as a challenge to seek out this information and perhaps during the process I would discover the identity of those five figures.

The following account is a record of how I set about trying to unravel a mystery whose twists and turns might well have graced a work of fiction.

During my investigations I came across an amazing number of premature deaths that must have been devastating to their close family members, and in some instances would have left wives and children with severe financial hardship.

My first line of enquiry was to speak to older members of the Harrison family, as Doreen had told me that prior to her parents moving into the Grange in 1945 an elderly lady by the name of Mrs Harrison had been living there.

She said that prior to their family moving in, a great deal of work had to be carried out internally due to the poor condition of the house.

None of the members of the Harrison family that I contacted knew exactly when the farm was acquired by their grandfather, Mr Luke Harrisson, nor did they know who he had purchased it from.

However they said that one of his sons by the name of Billy subsequently owned the farm, but later sold it on to the Co operative Wholesale Society.

I decided that my first step in the quest necessitated an examination of the entries listed in Kelleys and Whites Lincolnshire directories that related to Grimoldby, and discover who was farming at Grimoldby Grange at the time that each volume was published.

The temperature gauge in my car showed that the air temperature was -8 C on a desperately cold day in mid December 2010, as I parked my car and walked over ice covered paths to the warmth of Louth Library

In all they held volumes dating from 1851 to 1937, which seemed to vary in publishing intervals between four and ten years, with the average being about six years, though I am not certain if there had originally been other directories published for other years.

The loading bay of the creamery 1953

As I turned the pages and saw the names of the farmers who were farming at the Grange I started to feel quietly confident that I would very soon solve the mystery of the identity of the family on the photograph.

My initial optimism seemed to be fully justified when in the first directory that I examined for 1851; I found that a man by the name of Joshua Beverley and his wife Elizabeth were living at Grimoldby Grange. Was this the Beverly family I had discovered as tenants at the hall, I wondered?

Then when I discovered that his son Mathew Beverly was born in Grimoldby in 1839 and in due course inherited the Grange farm from his father, I felt that I was definitely moving in the right direction.

At the time of Kelley's 1868 directory Mathew Beverley was farming 210 acres, and employing 7 men on the farm, in addition to 4 maids in the house.

I felt sure that a family, who were employing that number of domestic servants, must be people of some means, as indicated by the quality of the ladies dresses in the photograph.

Subsequent volumes of the 1872, 1876 and 1882 directories indicate that Mathew increased the farm size to 510 acres, making him not only the largest landowner in Grimoldby, but certainly one of the major farmers in the Louth area.

So a man in his position with that number of staff would certainly give the appearance of the gentleman farmer portrayed in the photograph.

I now felt pretty certain that it must be Mathew Beverley with his wife and family who were standing proudly in front of their home.

I believed at that point that I had rather easily solved the identity of the family group, but never the less I thought that I needed to be one hundred per cent certain, so I felt that I ought to make a few final checks to confirm that my assumption was correct.

However my earlier euphoria was dented whilst checking the 1892 directory when I discovered that Mathew Beverleys name was no longer listed as farming at Grimoldby Grange. His name was replaced by the name of Mrs Beverley.

So where was Mathew?

Well a visit to Grimoldby church yard supplied me with the answer.

A large tomb set back from the right hand side of the path leading to the church door gave details of his father Joshuas death in 1866 and his mother Elizas death in 1877.

It was on a side panel where I came across my first instance of an untimely death. It records that his brother Edward and his wife Fanny, (a common contraction at the time for Francis,) had both been living little more than 250 yards away from Grimoldby Grange at the adjacent South Cockerington Hall, which incidentally is only a stone's throw from where I now live.

Edward died in 1866 aged only 42, and his wife fared little better as she died at South Cockerington Hall only 5 years later aged 52.

However on a badly eroded panel on the north side of the tomb I discovered that Mathew Beverley had also suffered a premature death aged 50 in 1889, whilst his wife Deborah continued to live until 1925 when she was 80 years of age.

In spite of Mathew Beverley's early death I still felt reasonably confident that the older man in the photograph must be him, and that the three other figures were almost certain to be his wife Deborah and their three children.

If the photograph had been taken around 1889 shortly before his death it would conveniently fit in with the time frame that I judged the photograph to have been taken.

As the directories only listed business people along with a few local notables, I had no idea of the age or sexes of Mathew's family, so sought the help of a good friend of mine Mr Tom Heys, who takes a keen interest in researching ancestral records.

Tom consulted the census data for 1881 and 1891, but the results were not the ones that I was expecting.

The census result for 1881 showed that Mathew, then aged 41 was married to his wife Deborah, then aged 34, and they had 3 young children aged from 2 years down to 1 month, but as they didn't have the older family that I was anticipating, my original optimism began to rapidly evaporate.

Irrespective of the children's ages there was another snag because they were all girls, and the photograph clearly showed a young man.

So we looked at the 1891 census which only confirmed that it was impossible for the photograph to be Mathew Beverley and his family.

The census stated that Deborah although still living at The Grange was a widow and she had 7 young children aged from 12 down to 4.

As they only had one son named Thomas, who would have been 6 at the time of his father's death, it was quite clear that the photograph could not have been Mathew Beverley with his son and 2 of his daughters because they would all have been far too young.

I became acutely aware of the tragic circumstances facing his 42 year old widow Deborah, who following her husband's early death at the age of 50 had to not only run the farm, but suffer the additional hardship of raising their 7 young children, especially as the oldest child was only 10 years of age at his death.

Back to Kellys directories once more and I discovered that Mrs Deborah Beverley is listed as being at the Grange for the following 15 years as indicated by the 1892, 1896 and 1905 editions.

But by the 1913 directory a Mr James Carter-White junior was listed as living there and farming the land.

However although the 1913 edition is the first time that James is mentioned, I notice that it's also the last reference to Herbert Carter White who had first appeared in 1896, when he is described as a farmer living and farming at The Glebe.

Interestingly the Glebe farm lies down a track at the western end of The Grange farm, and as long as I can remember it has been incorporated within the Grimoldby Grange farm.

I decided to examine the grave stones in Grimoldby churchyard and see if I could glean any further clues about the Carter Whites.

I came across the following inscription on one of the stones to the rear of the church yard.

Herbert Carter White 1870 – 1958 and his wife Jane 1866 – 1921, who lived their entire lives in this village.

So it became quite apparent that Herbert Carter White was at the very least the second generation of his family to live in Grimoldby, and in all probability would have had other decedents stretching even further back.

A magnificent granite cross stands imposingly to the left of the path as one approaches the church entrance and carry's the following inscription.

James Carter White of Grimoldby Grange.

Born March 8th 1867. Died August 5th 1922.

So who was James Carter White and where did he come from?

Tom consulted the census for 1901 and discovered that James Carter White was a widower then aged 34, with a 9 year old son also called James, and a 6 year old daughter by the name of Ruby.

James was obviously reasonably well off because at the time of the census he was living in one of the grander houses down Eleanor Street in Grimsby and was employing Mary White, his 55 year old cousin as a housekeeper along with 2 other servant girls to attend to the household's domestic duties.

The census revealed that he was a Chemist, and that he along with his cousin and both of the children were all born in Grimsby.

So if the man in the photograph wasn't Mathew Beverley could he be James Carter White I mused?

If the photograph had been taken in say 1912 James would have been 45, and his son James would then be aged 20.

Both of their ages would fit the figures in the photograph.

Could one of the young ladies have been his daughter Ruby who would then have been aged 17 and if so the other young woman might have been a friend of hers.

On that basis it would be reasonable to presume that the older woman could have been Mary his housekeeper cousin aged 66.

Yet somehow I'm not entirely convinced, as I am hypothesising about the other young woman, and further more the dress is more Victorian than Edwardian.

So I decided to check how long the Carter Whites were at The Grange and see if there might be another possibilities on who the figures could be.

At the 1911 census James was still listed as a widower aged 44 and now living in Grimoldby Grange with his 19 year old son James and 16 year old daughter Ruby.

But only 2 years later in 1913 Kelley records that James Carter White JUNIOR is listed as being at Grimoldby Grange whilst in 1919 his father James Carter White SENIOR is specifically mentioned as residing at Manby Grange.

James Carter White continues to be listed at Grimoldby Grange in 1919 and finally in 1922.

It seems certain however, that in spite of living in Grimsby, James Carter White must have had an earlier connection with Grimoldby because in 1900 he presented a stained glass memorial window to Grimoldby church in memory of his late wife, that's inscribed, "In memory of Emma White 1898".

So I've come across yet another tragedy, as James wife Emma was only 28 years old at the time of her death.

There is a further clue that James Carter White was active in Grimoldby at that time, because in 1907 he made a bet with Grimsby builder Sam Cartledge that he couldn't build a house in a working week.

So it's obvious that he must have owned The Grange farm at that time as Chestnut cottage which was the result, is situated by the roadside less than 100yards from the front of The Grange farm house.

A press report that I have come across describes James Carter White as being Lord of The Manor of Grimoldby, and goes on to detail how the builder's men starting on the Monday morning worked from dawn to dusk everyday to ensure that the building would have smoke coming out of the chimney by Saturday.

Although I have been unable to come across any records to support the theory, it seems highly likely to suppose that given the Carter Whites connection with Grimoldby that James or Herbert Carter White were involved in running the Grange farm soon after the death of Mathew Beverley in 1889.

James and his son continued to operate the farm until I discover yet another prematurely early death with the demise of James senior in 1922 at the age of 55.

Kelley shows that James Carter White junior was still at Grimoldby

Grange in 1922 but in the 1930 edition Luke Harrison, the grandfather of the Harrisons that I had contacted earlier was living there and farming the land.

It was at that point that I paid another visit to Grimoldby church yard hoping to discover a memorial to Luke Harrison, even though I realised that given the time that he came to the Grange in the late 1920s that it was most unlikely that it could be him on the photograph.

The day was bitterly cold with the remnants of the recent snow still lingering, as I examined gravestones to the rear of the church yard.

I had just read an inscription on my great grandparent's, John and Ann Smiths memorial that recorded the fact that they had lost a daughter aged 16, then another at 20, and finally the third of their 7 children had died aged 41, which was yet another instance of so many lives cut cruelly short.

My finger ends had begun to lose any feeling in the biting cold, so I was just about to abandon my search and head home for a warming cup of coffee when I made a remarkable discovery that changed everything.

I came across a grave stone partially hid by a spreading Yew tree that carried the following inscription.

Jane Ellison Harrison, died Occtober 9th 1946 aged 93 years.
Also Ruby her daughter died January 6th 1913 aged 26.
Also Gertrude her daughter died August 13th 1934.
Also Philip James her son killed in France July 1st 1916.
Also Philip Wallace her grandson killed in France aged 28.

My first thoughts were those of immense sorrow for the poor woman who had lost three of her children, which for all I knew were probably all the family that she had had.

I was coming across so many examples of young people who had died at quite a young age, and in this instance it was during their unfortunate mother's lifetime.

However the thing that really set my pulse racing was the fact that the ages of Jane along with her two daughters and son precisely matched the time frame of the figures in the photograph.

I felt certain that it had to be Jane Ellison Harrison on the photograph with her three children, but who was the man, and how could I prove my gut feeling.

Could Jane be the widow of Luke Edward Harrison I mused, and if so why wasn't his name listed on the stone?

With Tom Heys assistance we looked at the 1911 census and discovered that Luke Edward Harrison, although living in Kenwick Road at Louth and described as a farmer and cattle dealer had been born in Tealby in 1869.

But then when I gave it more thought I realised that Jane was unlikely to be his widow, as she must have been a generation older than Luke Edward as the inscription showed that she was born in 1853.

Yet she was called Harrison, and if my theory was correct, then what were Harrisons doing at The Grange in say 1907 when I already knew that the Carter Whites were there at around that time. Furthermore I knew that Luke Edward Harrison wouldn't be living there for another twenty years until after the Carter Whites.

There had to be another explanation, so it meant that I had to dig deeper and discover more about the Harrison family.

My theory of the man being Luke Edward collapsed when the 1911 census showed that his wife's name was Sarah and not Jane and that they had 4 sons and a daughter aged from 14 down to the youngest Billy who was aged only 1, in 1911.

Clearly the photograph wasn't of Luke Edward Harrisson and Sarah, along with their family because the children would all have been far too young even as late as 1920.

So we examined the 1881 census for Luke Edward Harrison and discovered that his father also called Luke was farming 600 acres in Tealby, 15 miles away in North Lincolnshire and employing 8 labourers, in addition to 2 boys.

He was the head of a large family of 10 children, and that one of his sons was named Luke Edward Harrison with the same birth date as the Luke Edward that we had discovered was living in Louth in 1911, so we were obviously dealing with the right person.

His wife Betsy had 2 domestic servants to help her in the house along with a governess.

Then success, we discovered that the governess who they were employing to educate the children was named JANE ELLISON MURDOCK, and was listed as being a single woman aged 37, born 1844 in Bristol.

With the name Ellison and the same birth date she had to be the same woman who was buried in Grimoldby church yard.

We then looked for Jane Ellison Harrison on the 1911 census and discovered that she was living at 11 Littlefield Lane in Grimsby, and sure enough she had two daughters; Ruby and Gertrude.

However I then came across yet another tragedy in what was turning out to be a repetitive catalogue of early deaths, because she was now a widow and renting out rooms in her home to supplement her income.

But I still needed to know why she was called Harrison, so Tom studied records of deaths and marriages and discovered that the older Luke Harrison who had originally employed Jane as a governess, lost his wife Betsy at the early age of 45 in 1882.

Once again I've come across another instance of a tragically early death.

Records disclose that following her marriage to Luke in 1864 she had a child each year commencing in 1866 for the following 10 years.

As the cause of her death is unrecorded we can only speculate that it may have been as a result of the constant trauma of repetitive childbirth.

Whatever the cause, Luke married Jane the governess little more than a year after Betsy's death, but strangely the marriage was conducted in Norwich.

The 1891 census disclosed that he had started a new family because in addition to 5 members of his first family living with him and Jane, they now had 2 children of their own, shortly to be followed by a third, judging by the gravestone recording Gertrudes death.

We discovered that only 9 years later in 1900 that Luke had died at the age of 62, and presumably it was at that point that Jane his widow moved to Grimsby with her three children.

Now it can't just be a coincidence that James Carter White a widower should be living in one of the smarter houses in Eleanor Street Grimsby, a little over half a mile from where Jane Harrison a widow was living in one of the grand houses down Littlefield Lane, and that they both came to Grimoldby where they are buried, albeit in differing parts of the church yard.

I believe that the photograph is of James Carter White senior standing on the left, along with Jane Ellison Harrison and her three children.

I think that the photograph was quite likely taken in the summer (judging by the flowering shrubs in the background) of possibly 1907 or 1908,), at about the same time that James moved into Grimoldby Grange.

Everything about this analysis fits. James would have been aged 41, and Jane 54. Ruby the elder daughter was then 21, and her sister Gertrude 16. Philip her son would have been aged 18.

It seems more than likely that the two families may have become friendly in Grimsby, and as they had each lost their respective spouses James could have invited Jane along with her three children to view his new home.

Jane must have come to live in Grimoldby either through a friendship with James Carter White senior or by virtue of her stepson Luke Edward moving there in the mid 1920s, or indeed a combination of both factors.

After almost half a century few people realise that Grimoldby Grange was once the nerve centre for an industrial facility that proved to be the financial salvation of not only the next owner of Grimoldby Grange but also many local farmers.

Milk being processed from the churns. Photo courtesy Mrs D Partridge

During the 1920s Mr Luke Edward Harrison, in spite of being profoundly deaf was running a successful business as a cattle dealer in the Louth area when he purchased the Grimoldby Grange farm from James Carter-White in about 1927.

However as the severe economic depression deepened following the Wall Street crash in 1929 he was struggling to keep his head above water, at a time when farmers and other businesses throughout the country were going bankrupt almost daily.

Billy Harrison, the youngest of Luke's three sons and a daughter, left the family home to take up a career in the retail clothing industry.

From the onset he was industrious, and was determined to make a fortune in whatever opportunity presented itself. Discovering the price that people were willing to pay for mushrooms, particularly out of season, he found a disused railway tunnel that he was able to rent cheaply and soon built up a thriving business growing mushrooms.

However it was largely because of the parlous state of agriculture in 1931 that Billy Harrison, returned to Grimoldby to aid his father stave off bankruptcy, and try to make the farm viable by introducing a new enterprise at Grimoldby Grange that would extend the value of what the farm was producing.

The inter war years were a period of severe economic hardship for farmers, when the agricultural industry was plunged into yet another disastrous depression.

To the scores of small farmers in the marsh villages who eked out a living by milking a handful of cows, the construction of a local milk factory that would collect their churns of milk on a daily basis, would make all the difference between surviving and going out of business.

The plant would give an immediate benefit to the profitability of the Granges own milking herd, and be an excellent local outlet for the much larger specialist milking herds such as those of A & F W Borrill at South Cockerington Grange.

In 1932 Billy contacted Mr Frank Borrill who was not only farming at South Cockerington Grange, but was also the NFU secretary at Louth.

He requested Mr Borrill to accompany him to the newly created Milk Marketing Boards headquarters at Thames Ditton near London, to try and obtain permission from the MMB, who had recently been granted a monopoly in respect of the purchase and sale of milk, to set up a milk processing factory at Grimoldby Grange.

Two large milk tanks being installed in 1952

David Brown milking the Granges Ayrshire cows 1953

Billy realised that the best way to extract extra value from his father's herd of milk cows was to process the milk into cheese and butter. In order to do that he reasoned that if he also purchased milk from the many small milk producers in the area, that he would also benefit by processing a larger volume, and so would be able to justify building a larger unit.

Clearly with Mr Borrills help they were successful in their application as it led to Billy constructing a modern small dairy factory, which by the end of 1933 was producing butter and cheese and drying the skimmed milk to produce milk powder.

The business prospered to such a degree that before long Billy Harrison had expanded his dairy enterprise by purchasing Sutterton dairies near Boston, when he installed his brother Gordon as manager. His next acquisition was the purchase of Lincoln and Carlton dairies near Lincoln, followed by other milk processing factories and retail rounds in other parts of the country.He sold the Grimoldby factory at the height of its productivity to the Co-operative society in 1945, though by that time they had ceased to manufacture cheese, and were now concentrating on making butter and dried milk powder.

It became a common sight whilst travelling around the marsh villages during the 1940s and 1950s to see one or two metal milk churns standing on a wooden platform alongside most farm gates and the red painted milk lorries making their rounds.

Mr Marriott was appointed the Co ops first manager, and remained in that position for the next 10 years, when he left to purchase a farm in North Yorkshire.

Mr Brown a Loughborough man succeeded Mr Marriott as general manager for the farm and dairy factory in1953.   He had first moved to Lincolnshire in 1941 as a farm manager.

The factory had ceased making cheese quite early in its life, but continued to make butter and dried milk powder up to the time of its closure.

Following the decision to close the milk factory in 1963, the Co op decided to run the farm on purely commercial lines growing arable crops.

The original farm house with its turreted battlements over double bay windows at the front of the house, occupied a similar position to where Mr and Mrs Grantham's new house now stands.

Ann Stubbs, nee Brown, who grew up in the old house whilst her father was manager explained to me that the house had a reputation for being haunted, though she never saw any apparitions.   She enjoyed her time there as a teenager, reasoning that as it was always a happy home the paranormal were kept at bay.

She remarked that few people knew of the secret passage that led to the domestic quarters at the rear of the house, which may have something to do with folk seeing ghostly encounters, and might even be the origin of some misdeed in the past.

It would be convenient to think that the haunted stories had something to do with the untimely deaths of Mathew Beverley and his brother, but I suspect that it goes back much further as a the mock battlements erected to the front of the house indicate that it was merely a facade in front of a much older property.

On the 23rd of August 1963 the Grimsby Evening Telegraph reported that the Co-operative Wholesale Society's creamery at The Grange, Grimoldby, would close down on the 30th of September.

After 33 years production, Mr John Brown, who had been manager for the previous 10 years explained that the reason for closure "was because of falling milk production in the Eastern Counties, coupled with decreased demand".

He added, "when I first went to Grimoldby we were handling seven times as much milk and had a staff of 15, but this has now dwindled to 10".

Mr Brown went on to explain that "the creamery dealt with 'accommodation' milk, supplying the society at Grimsby, Scunthorpe, Long Eaton, Retford, Gainsborough and other towns over a wide area. It's now the policy of the Milk Marketing Board to supply the retail societies direct".

The Browns were the last family to live in the original Grange house, so that after they left in 1964 the house fell into disrepair.

In November 1977 the 333 acre farm was put up for auction by Wm H Brown at the council chambers in Louth Town Hall.

The Co-operative Wholesale society explained that the reason for sale was because they were expanding their farming activities elsewhere.

Mr Robert Coy who farmed extensively in the Sleaford area, and was the owner of Sharps seeds became the new owner and continued to farm the land in a similar manner to that of the CWS, growing solely arable crops.

Mr Bob Lowis became the working farm Forman with backup from Sleaford at busy times in the farming year.

The burden of distance made it difficult for Mr Coy and his 2 sons to make a success of the farm, so it was sold once again in 1986 when it was purchased by Mr David Grantham.

CHAPTER TWENTY THREE
Aeons of time

The observations that I have recorded in this book are rather like waiting at a level crossing at night and seeing a brilliantly illuminated passenger train speed past. An observer waiting on the track side is only able to catch fleeting glimpses of a few of the passengers who are reading writing, talking, eating, or doing many other activities cocooned within their carriages. The passengers meanwhile are completely oblivious to what's happening in the world outside of the train. So it is with these brief observations from Conscience Hill when viewed from a geological perspective. They are glimpses of some of the life and times that have occurred in the blink of an eye, but to me it has been a lifetime.

My father often remarked that as a result of a geological survey conducted during the 1930s that the Nottinghamshire coalfields extended eastwards under the Lincolnshire marsh and out into the North Sea. They were so deep that it would be totally uneconomic to sink mine shafts here, even if the engineering skills existed to reach the massive depths of the coal seams. And there the matter rested until a time during the late 1950s when we were approached by contractors who were carrying out a seismological study to determine the geology of the rock strata of the mid marsh area, presumably with a view to determine exactly how deep the hydro carbon deposits were.

I remember that shortly after, a drilling rig on the back of a lorry drilled a matrix of holes over the farm and the surrounding area and then detonated an explosive charge down the holes with sufficient force to rattle crockery in Hill House. The drilled holes left a depression that was capped with a concrete slab, and earth was finally filled over the excavated area. In the early 80s the local press buzzed with speculation in anticipation of an 'oil Klondike' when a drilling rig operated by BP drilled an exploratory well at the Howdales road junction. In spite of numerous technical difficulties the well was deemed to be dry, resulting in the entire infrastructure of hard standings and fencing that surrounded the drill site being completely cleared away in order that the top soil from the site area could be replaced and the field returned to agriculture. In 1995 a management buyout took place and drilling recommenced on the same site, resulting in the discovery of commercial quantities of natural gas. To the accompaniment of a sound not dissimilar to the high pitched roar of a jet engine at full throttle the first well was test flared in December 1995 when it completely illuminated the surrounding area to a radius of more than four miles. In 1997 a land planning consultant working for Candeca Resourses Ltd which was a wholly owned subsidiary of Morrison Middlefield Resources Ltd, a Canadian company approached us wishing to drill an exploratory gas well in our field at the end of Stewton Lane, pretty well opposite where the Hoyes old farm house used to stand. They pointed out to us that we should immediately dispel any thoughts of becoming oil barons as the state owned all mineral rights and the most remuneration that we could expect was an annual ground rent linked to agricultural production with no guarantee on the condition of the land when it was returned to us.

Although they found natural gas which has to be constantly flared off, they discovered to their surprise that the well contained small quantities of light crude oil which led to the installation of storage tanks in order that it could be taken away by tanker to the oil refinery. Later that year they commenced a seismic survey using IMC Geophysics Ltd with their specialist four wheel drive vibrosis vehicles, using the very latest "3D" techniques to map underground structures suitable for trapping oil and gas. We were told that seismic surveys operate in a similar way to the echo sounding techniques used both by fishermen to locate fish and in medical ultra sound scanning. A convoy of four specialised vehicles known as Vibrosis Units sent sound waves into the earth, which reflected the sound from the many layers of geological rock before transmitting the echoes back to a network of sensitive geophones on the surface. The reflected sound, was amplified and relayed back to special recording instruments in a control vehicle. As a result of the seismic survey other sites in the locality of Howdales were identified and new drilling sites established, the most important of which was adjacent to the 40 acres of land that we purchased in August 1991, when it became the nerve centre of the new gas field.

Rather like demolishing a house, starting at the top by removing the roof, followed by successive layers of building materials that mirrors the houses construction, so the drill from a towering drilling rig passed through successive layers of sediments. Each layer representing a geological period as the lower it drilled the further back in time it went. The geology of the area was confirmed by the core samples resulting from drilling that first well. It went down to a depth of over 2500 meters and finally entered the gas bearing sandstone areas of rocks laid down over 300 million years ago in the Westphallan period.

Going back in time, the drill left the modern era as it passed through a relatively narrow thickness of clay deposited by a shallow sea that receded some 10,000 years ago, before it entered a thick layer of chalk that outcrops in the present day Lincolnshire Wolds, followed by Lower Cretacecous sands that took the drilled depth to a little over 200 meters.

Massive layers of Kimmeridge, Ampthill and Oxford clays continued down to the 590 meter contour followed by about 20 meters of Lincolnshire Limestone that outcrops today along the Lincoln edge when the depth reached 610 meters. Liss clays laid down in the Jurrasic period met the drill at 900 meters with Mercia Mudstone extending to the 1150 meter level, closely followed by Sherwood Sandstone down to nearly 1500 meters which was laid down in the Triassic period. A succession of relatively thin layers of rocks including more limestone was laid down in the Permian period finishing at 1900 meters below ground level. Now in the Westphalian period the drill passed through Wickersley&Ackworth rock on either side of the 2000 meter contour. It then continued down to Brinsley Abdy rock before striking a layer of Top Hard coal at 2150 meters, interspersed with more layers of the above rock and Silkstone coal around the 2200 meter level. The drill finally passed into the first rocks of the Early Westphalian gas reservoirs that comprised sediments which were laid down over 300 million years ago in a river/delta complex flowing from the northeast that would have looked very similar to the present day Mississippi Delta flowing into the Gulf of Mexico.

In 2001 the centre of operations known as Saltfleetby B Site needed an extension in area so that more wells could be sunk down to an increased depth of almost 3500 meters, and as four of the six acres that we had purchased in 1991 was the most suitable for the expansion, we entered into another agreement on similar terms to that entered into at the Stewton end of the farm.

The fragility of human existence seems incredibly puny when viewed in the context of the hundreds of millions of years that have elapsed since these gas bearing rocks were a part of a swampy river estuary

CHAPTER 22
Conscience Hill March 10TH 2011

It's one of those clear sunny days in early spring with a stiff breeze blowing from the North West and I'm standing on the top of Conscience Hill looking out over the Marsh to the east of me.

I tug my coat a little tighter around my body mindful that the wind still has an edge of winter about it as I ponder on the thoughts and aspirations of people who down the ages have stood on this very spot. With a feeling of detachment from everyday life they like me have gazed over the surrounding panoramic scene when they must also have had thoughts similar to mine.

As I walked along Stewton Lane on my journey up here it was obvious that the suns powerful elixir of life was working its magic, with the first hint of green to be seen emerging from the swollen hedgerow buds. Along the roadside, early spring wild flowers were hesitantly showing colour. I suppose it's on occasions such as this that epitomises why farmers are ever optimists, because irrespective of whatever has occurred during the previous year, spring is a fresh start. Rather like a recharged battery, the lengthening hours of daylight extend our feeling of well being at the commencement of another farming year with the excitement of rebirth, as crops spring into growth and new calves are born almost daily. Paradoxically the agricultural optimism of a new farming year is at odds with the economic pessimism that the rest of the economy is experiencing as the recession deepens. The profitibility of agriculture has always been affected by the unpredictability of the weather, linked to a long production cycle. For example anyone purchasing one of our young bulls is unlikely to see the first calf born until almost a year later. Then they will have to wait in all probability for a further two years before they can market their first finished beef animal, entailing a delay of almost three years from making their first investment. Similarly there can be a delay of more than a year with a crop of grain from the time that the seed is planted until the resultant crop is marketed. Farmers must have a high degree of blind faith, or they would almost certainly never embark on such a perilous course of investment, attempting to produce a product whose market price is influenced not only by the laws of supply and demand but also by the political agendas of politicians. As the New Year gathers pace the optimism that's now prevalent with the much higher commodity prices will continue. Farmers will recall how the higher prices in 2007 left a legacy of much higher input costs as the price of diesel reached values that exceeded anyone's most pessimistic forecasts during the high usage period of the 2008 harvest/autumn cultivation period. The price of fertilisers and chemicals followed suit creating a position where the profitability of growing crops was to say the least marginal. Yet we farmers are ever optimists. In spite of the world's economic turmoil we are undaunted. We continue with the yearly cycle of planting and harvesting, taking a pragmatic long term view that the land, of which we are temporary custodians, will still be growing food in the time of our children's children stretching away into the century's ahead.

As I retrace my footsteps home, I can't help wondering if all the events that I have witnessed from the backdrop of Conscience Hill, will soon have passed from living memory and will melt into history along with all the other figures who have stood here and reminisced in a similar manner about people and places that they have known.

HENRY SMITH'S
letters to his sisters

In October 1887, after more than a year in USA, Henry my maternal grandfather writes from South Haven on the shore of Lake Michigan to his younger, and probably favourite sister, Fanny who was born 3 years after him in 1865.

Dear sister,
Just a line or two hoping you well as leaves me at present. Well we have got all our peaches off, all but one tree. We had 580 trees left last Saturday. It is terrible cold here today. We have got apples to get off yet and a little more work when I suppose I shall have to be looking out for somewhere else. It's all shifting over here, for if we get 8 months in a place we do real well. I was glad to hear from you and that you were well and that you had joined the chapel I wonder if Brother John is a member yet. I hope he is well. I can't say a deal about myself, I seem to get on in some way, I suppose fate rules all or I should not have been here. I often think a good deal.
We have had some bad storms of late. There was a boat wreck here a week ago today when 6 or 7 drowned. Mr Plummer and I went to another wreck at night but none were drowned. They have only had coast guards here this summer for the first time so they have not yet had a deal of practice. They can only sail on the lake for 8 months as it freezes over during the winter. I don't care for the winter here. I can do with the summer but it is like freezing the life out you during the winter.
I had Joe up here last Monday as he was going to town; he is going to stick it out for another year. He is going a bit further off. I scarcely see him because I have to work on Sundays as our boat does not run on the Saturday as they will not sell them, (peaches), on the Sunday. It goes out on Sunday nights and gets into Chicago at 5 am on Monday morning. It is 90 miles from South Haven, so you can see if it takes them 8 hours; it is just the same as the London market with you.
It is the largest city in America.
I have a good (shot) gun. I got it from Dave Marshall,--he owed me £1

so I gave him another £1 for it but I have been bid £3 for it. That's what he gave for it, but I would not sell it. He was bad off when he left here. You must say not a thing about what I have said – I should not like for him to know I said anything, but it is their own fault if they don't want to get on here. He is wild and although I was fond of him he lied against me. I have not been to see his brother Jim.

I will bring you a few skins off the animals that I shoot. This last 2 months I have been so busy.

It will soon be the fair at Louth, I shall not be there, or you, I think. They will get on without us. I was glad to hear that they were getting on well at home and that they are well in health too. You will think this is a short letter but I will send you a paper or two so that you will get to know the news as I don't seem to have a deal to tell you this time. When you write back you must tell me where brother John is at work and where he harvested and what they pay per day as I am thinking of coming back if they pay 4 shillings per day [20p]. I fear they are not doing that well.

Dear, I shall have to quit this time. I sent mother a letter last week and 2 of my photos, I hope that they will answer it if they have time, but I expect they are busy. I was sorry to hear of such a bad accident at Doncaster. Well I must say goodbye, I remain your affectionate brother.

H. Smith.

Henry wrote the following letter to his elder, widowed sister Eliza, born 1854. From Davisville - near Sacramento, California.

Davisville. December 30 1894.
Dear Sister,
I now take the pleasure of answering your kind and welcome letter which I received and was glad to know you were well but was very sorry to hear of poor Stephen Boswell-what a blow to his poor young wife and child and so sudden. We notice it the more I suppose if you have had a merry Christmas. I hope so well it did not make any difference.

We work all Christmas day but went to Davisville on Christmas Eve to see the Christmas tree and hear the children recite pieces. It was held in a large hall when all the different churches joined together instead of each having a tree of their own. The choir sang suitable chorals followed by the brass band which kept playing selections during the evening while they handed the presents off the tree. Anyone could put a present on the tree for another. As they were all ticketed some of the men got a pair of socks, some a house and some a baby which made a good deal of laughter. Altogether we had a very enjoyable evening. Every village that is large enough has its brass band. We have a very good one in Davisville, they play for a public dance in the hall every two weeks in the winter, and once a month in the summer choosing a good moonlight night, as they have it in the picnic grove where they have a large platform erected on purpose. We are having a very wet winter this far. It has rained nearly continually for the last month. We have not been able to do any sowing as yet. I should be glad if it would fair up for a few days so we could get our hay in as it is past time for it now. The other grain, it does not matter about for another month.

We have 8 mule teams so it will not take us long when it fairs up. We have another 2 teams belonging to our neighbour who is going to help us and then we will help him. As he has all low land now under water we can sow our land before his is ready.

The roads are in a terrible condition, I never saw them worse, as they are knee deep with mud in a good many places, and almost impassable.

The boys are playing cards; they play the whole of Sunday and rainy days too and never tire of it. I never play them as I cannot see any fun in them. Give me a gun and my pair of dogs, and the cards and profanity can go. However I have had a very poor winter this far having only killed one solitary duck for they have been scarce this winter, still I have shot several hare and cotton tail rabbit. I caught an owl with horns about a month ago. I had it in the barn till this week when it died. I let it have its liberty as they are great mouse catchers and it used to fight all the dogs and cats on the place, and it could whip them too. I caught a Butcher bird last week and had it in a cage until last night when the old cat pulled the bottom out and let it fly away. They are about the size of your blackbird, but they will kill birds and snakes and almost anything. They very pretty, closely resemble the jay in colour.

Tiny has four puppies; I have given two of them away, the others I shall have to put down because nobody wants them. I've had to put down my old greyhound too because he was so lame.

We had a very cold week last; the mountains are all covered in snow to within 15 miles of us.

I am healing vinegar and salt to doctor my chilblains with, for I always get my feet frost bitten when I wear rubber boots and I have to have them in the winter as my cow corral is knee deep in mud. They cost me £1 per pair, they would not last over 3 months if I were to wear them steady. As soon as it dries a little I put on my shoes.

My saddle horse died last week, he was took sick and died within half a day even though he was only a young horse. I broke him when I first came here and had rode him ever since. I felt very sorry when he died for I had got greatly attached to him but he was always a treacherous one, a genuine Brouko, but they make the best saddle horses we have, but we have no more of the kind. I have got another, (horse), we raised ourselves, a very pretty gentle thing three years old. I had not the heart to put the old horses bridle on her for I always rode him in a Spanish bit and they are very cruel, but you cannot get anything too cruel for a Brouko. We sold a pair of horses this week for £11 each for draying purposes, if it had been in England they would have made £80 each as I saw them sold when I was at home. They weighed 1800 lbs each. We bought a pair of little mules by adding only another £1 more, the two of them only weighed as much as one of the horses, but everything is only half as dear as it was two years ago. We have eighty turkeys to sell but we can only get 4 pence halfpenny per pound live weight and so have not sold but I don't think we shall get anymore. We ate one on thanksgiving and another on Christmas day, and we have had another today for it is cheaper than to buy beef at 5 pence per lb. We have been living on spareribs ever since we killed pigs till I am tired of seeing them.

Well I suppose you will get tired of reading but time goes so slow and my pen fast for it is only ½ past 7 now and I don't go to bed before half past eight. If I could only write my summer letters now it would be more pleasant to me, however we must not complain but be thankful for our health and strength. I would like to have spent the Christmas at home with you for I know you would have a joyous time but hope to meet again. Wish you all a happy and prosperous new year. Had a very nice letter from cousin Anna Borrill all well except Uncle who is only poorly she says and has been all summer.

So goodbye with best wishes to you all from your loving brother,
H. Smith.

From 10th October 1893 until December 1894 Henry earned $495. During the calendar year 1st January 1894 to January 1895 he records earning $420, then Henry writes again to his older sister, Eliza, from Davisville on January 27th, with an addition on February 6th 1896.

Dear Sister

I now take the opportunity to write these few lines to you hoping they will find you all enjoying good health as leaves me only very poor at the present time. Well I have been very sick, I had a very bad spell with my mouth, it cost me £12 to get my teeth filled, and new ones put in for I had the toothache so bad I could do nothing and I have had them pulled so often that I had not so many left so I had either to have the rest pulled and a set of false ones put in, or have the old ones filled up but it cost a lot of money to get them fixed, so I am glad to get them done with, for they were a lot of pain.

Well we are having a terrible winter I never saw so much wet. We have not had scarce a fine day since it started which was the first of November. The snow in the mountains is terrible; the trains are stopped in the snow and have been for 15 days. There are about 5000 men shovelling to clear the track but it is a difficult job. There was a terrible accident last night a little below here. A train was run off the track on account of the water undermining the road, both the driver and fireman was killed.

No trains came into Davisville yesterday or today on account of the track been washed away. The oldest man here never saw so much wet before, everything is flooded between here and Sacremento. It is nothing but one vast sea for the river burst the bank and with the rain it is fearful on the bits of high places. Horses have been fed out of boats for weeks while the rabbits and small animals have been drowned by the hundreds. I see the rabbits on a bit of high ground as big as a house floor; hundreds of them running about too afraid to jump in the water and be drowned for it is like looking across the sea. All you can see is the trees for the tops of fences are all under water and now if it turns warm and the snow melts in the mountains I am afraid we shall have such a flood in this valley as was never known. Before we can see the mountains all covered with snow. There has been terrible suffering and loss of life I will send a picture or two home. I sent you one at the time of the bank in the river; I suppose you got it alright. I was very sorry to hear of aunt's death but still it comes and there is no stopping it. We have had 2 very sudden deaths here these last few days. Our roads are knee deep with mud, I wish it would dry up for my horses feet are so sore and I cannot get them well, they are all the time in the mud, for we are not like you having good roads.

We have to be content with mud, but still they will do, in the summer they are all dust, but there is always something, we have to make the best of it.

The Mrs and daughter are down with the influenza which is very bad here. Well we are having a little better weather now I have sent some papers home to show you what the weather is like here in the mountains but of course the weather here in the plains is altogether different for it is not cold here. Well I must tell you I had a bad accident with the horse. I left the ranch and went to Sacremento till I got better. Am not altogether right but am at work. I could not get in hospital so the doctor got me a bed in a private family. I was in bed 8 days. I was operated on at ½ past 3 and laid stark and cold while 9 when I began to feel a little warm in my feet and gradually came round.

I don't mind about being cut open but it is fairly rough when they sew you up, but I got the best doctor there was in town. The woman waited on me herself, for I hate to have a man wait on me, but the days seem like years, but they were very kind to me. They had two daughters; they would bring me fruit in at a night but would not speak of course.

When I got up the mother gave me an introduction to each of them and then I had plenty of company, but here you cannot speak to a girl until you have had an introduction for it would be insulting, and when you meet a girl you are acquainted with you always touch your hat, in fact it is about the same as your masters daughters and the young gents that come there to see them.

Here they always speak of a woman as a lady, whether she works or not, but these people were well off, not rich but in good circumstances.

It cost me a lot of money but so long as I did not die it is alright. I would take no opiate but had to take a few pills to allay the pain.

When they got through there was two of them, the doctor and his assistant. He would not let me eat anything but a little oatmeal and milk. You can bet I had a feast when I got up.

I used to go to the theatre (?) every night and fill my sides out with the best grub in the land besides spending a good deal of time with my girl.

Well I paid my bill and left very friendly for they made me promise to come and see them every time I come to town if I was satisfied with their treatment. Of course I was very glad to make their acquaintance as there is nobody that would have cared for me as they did, for it is bad work for a woman to have a man bedfast and a stranger at that. But she had a good deal more sense than a good many for there was no bustle about her, and she could have waited on a dozen more beside me, but then I never made a trouble of it, if I died I could not help it.

There is no use to trouble and annoy people about. She would sit on the bed and chat when I had not too much pain and keep things quiet when I was.

I should have wrote to you before I was operated on and thought it would only trouble you and nearly kill mother if she heard of it, and there is no use to trouble her. Please burn this when you have read and not let mother know and oblige.

Give my love to all.
Your ever loving & affectionate brother,
H. Smith.

These letters were found in a little casket, along with other personal effects, after the death of my mother in 2004

My thanks are extended to: Paul Hope for allowing me to use information that he gathered for his millennium book entitled "A brief History of South Cockerington".

Tom Heys for providing me with details of the research that he has carried out into the Needham Family Tree and Grimoldby Grange families.

John and Maureen Lill for reading the manuscript and giving me enthusiastic encouragement.

For the loan of photographs from those acknowledged under them but above all my grateful thanks are expressed to Miranda France, who due to a chance encounter when she sought my help researching details about Charolais Cattle for her novel 'Hill Farm' (to be published Spring 2011), encouraged me to write this book.

Above All I wish to thank Tom Cann and all at Tucann Design & Print for their friendship and invaluable advice.

Ralph Needham March 2011

Ralph, knowing his roots, always had a great respect for ordinary country folk and their daily struggles. His research opened up veins of intrigue where some families became very rich and others strained to survive, this led him to write 'Mantrap' a novel.
Here is a sample.
Tom Cann, publisher

MANTRAP
By Ralph Needham

Mantrap is the first book in a trilogy that follows the fortunes of two families. The Vavours living in the grand Hall and the Slades eking out a living as very poor cottage farmers. The story commences in 1795 when William Vavour acquires the estate through more than a hint of sharp practice, from an old established family who had lived in the village since Norman times.

David Ingelby, is a lawyer in a small market town in Lincolnshire, and will do almost anything for money, so he is quite happy to go along with Williams wishes to evict Bill Slade and his family from their cottage and few acres of land that have been in their possession for centuries. By evicting these poor people he sets in train a sequence of events that don't reach a conclusion until after The Great War, 125 years later.

The incredibly hard farming life that succeeding generations of Slades endure, is set against the wealth and abuse of privilege that the Vavours enjoy in the estates great Hall. The action is set near Hoult, a small town in rural Lincolnshire, against a backdrop of major wars and the way that the industrial revolution spawned the introduction of labour saving machines to farms removing some of the backbreaking drudgery.

MANTRAP
April 27th 1920

His fear of heights stemmed from childhood when his father rescued him from the high branches of an old oak in the corner of the farmyard. The position hadn't improved as he got older. In fact it was probably worse, because a reoccurring theme of his dreams seemed to revolve around him being in a high place in imminent danger of falling to his death. He generally woke up terrified, unsure for a few moments exactly where he was, convinced he had lost his grip on the windowsill of a tall building or was sliding to oblivion over a cliff face.

But he certainly wasn't dreaming now, as he stood twenty five feet above the ground, on the corner of a straw stack, with only a wooden fork shaft for support. It was little wonder therefore that he felt unsafe, when familiar objects on the ground looked a long way down from this perspective.

It took all his resolve to stand on the sloping edge of the stack and plunge the two foot, razor sharp, cutting knife into the straw, in order that he could cut a square of straw. His feeling of unease wasn't improved by the knowledge that whilst carrying out a similar manoeuvre, his grandfather slipped and suffered a fatal fall. His heart pounded, as turning towards the wooden ladder, he gingerly lowered a foot, hoping to find the security of a rung but midway through the manoeuvre he glanced in the direction of the Hall, just in time to see his elderly neighbour collapse on the gravel drive.

"I saw you fall", Andrew said, by way of explanation, as forgoing his reassuring grip on the fork shaft for the sides of the ladder, he made a hurried decent and raced to the old man's assistance.

"I am so grateful, you're so very kind", Charles Vavour said as Andrew helped him to a sitting position.

Andrew retrieved Charles's top hat and walking stick, then with the back of his hand, brushed a patch of dust from the old man's black frock coat.

From his carefully groomed silver hair to his black boots, that shone with all the intensity of black diamonds, Charles Vavour always dressed with the sartorial elegance befitting a man living in the Hall.

"Let me help you to your feet, then you can sit down over there", Andrew said pointing to a garden seat, bearing a lot number for the following day's sale.

"It's so very kind of you", Charles repeated, still visibly shaken by his fall.

"You probably caught a foot in one of these", Andrew said, kicking a tussock of grass that had taken root in the gravel drive.   Still dazed from his fall, Charles raised his eyes and looked at what had once been a carefully tended island of lawn in the centre of the drive, but was now an overgrown jungle of weeds.

"Do you think you can manage to walk across to the house and perhaps have a drink"? Andrew said after a while.

Emotion welled inside him at the kind consideration shown to him by a man whose family had suffered appalling atrocities at the hands of his forbears. He looked back at the Hall, his ancestral home, and saw the boarded windows, set on either side of a flight of steps leading to two perfectly proportioned Corinthian columns flanking the doorway, above which, the figure of a winged Eagle carved in finest Portland stone, gazed defiantly in the direction of the hills to the west.

Spotting the marquee in the court yard reminded Andrew that everything, including the very fabric of the building, would very soon be gone, as once the sale of the contents was complete workman would begin the task of demolishing the building.

"I was born here you know", Charles said with a backward glance at the Hall's impressive west front. "I remember as a child how my sisters and I loved to play hide and seek. There were so many places to hide".

"Didn't Aunt Kate come here when she was learning to play the piano"?

"My dear Kate", Charles sighed. "Everyone liked her. When she died something died in me also, though I still had the boys until; --- until I lost both of them as well".

"I know", Andrew said lightly touching Charles shoulder. "That time will remain with me forever".

"I can never thank you enough for what you did. I don't know why I ever doubted your word".

As the details of that sordid episode came back to him, a tear rolled down his face on to the collar of his coat. Charles continued to reminisce, as they both walked steadily the hundred or so paces to the farmhouse.

"I remember as quite a young boy how excited I felt when I caught my first fish in the lake. I couldn't wait to rush home and show it to Father. I always got on well with him, which may have had something to do with the fact that I was the only boy in a family of girls. I never felt the trepidation experienced by my sisters who held him in awe as they were often frightened by his authoritarian manner".

Charles stopped in his tracks and a frown came over his face as though he was recalling an unsettling incident from the deeper recesses of his memory.

"I remember another occasion though, for quite a different reason. It was a sunny, spring day, towards the end of March, with a stiff north westerly wind that made it feel quite cool. Mother insisted I wore a coat when I went for a walk in the bottom wood.

The beck had recently been in flood following heavy rain on the hills and now that the water level had subsided, pebbles under the water glinted as sunlight slashed through the branches of the trees.

As I picked my way through the cow parsley on the bank top, something caught my attention lying partially exposed in the bed of the stream. I scrambled down the bank and gingerly stepped into the streams stony bottom which at that point was only ankle deep.

I discovered the object that had aroused my curiosity was not a piece of unusually worn stone, as I had at first presumed, but was made of metal. I took hold of what I thought looked like a piece of brown cord attached to the strange looking object, and gave it a sharp tug".

"What had you found?" Andrew asked, as he opened the farmhouse door enabling Charles to pass into the scullery. "Go in the kitchen and take a seat by the fire, I'll give Martine a call.

Another door opened and an attractive young woman holding a baby emerged into the kitchen.

"Charse ow good to see you", Martine said, her eyes sparkling as she gave him a broad smile.

Passing her infant son to Andrew, she warmly embraced the old man, lightly kissing him on either cheek.

"It seems no time since I saw you two being married in Bethincourt", Charles said clearly delighted to meet the young Frenchwoman. Glancing in the direction of the baby lying contentedly in Andrews's arms, added

"What name have you chosen for him"

"Philippe"! Martine replied.

"It seemed only right to name him in memory of Martine's brother". Andrew said. "After all if it hadn't been for his documents, it's most unlikely I would be here now".

Andrew explained about Charles's fall, while Martine methodically set about cleaning a graze to his hand.

"You were telling me about something you found in the beck", Andrew said.

Much perkier now with colour returning to his cheeks, Charles said "Of course, the cross, it's played such an important part in the lives of our two families".

"In some ways the object I found resembled the cross that mother wore on a gold chain around her neck, but this one had two bars of unequal length running across the vertical and had some kind of inscription inscribed in the metal.

When I rubbed it against my coat it revealed a silver colour and I was able to decipher a capital, "S" followed by "auny".

"Le croix de Lorraine", Martine said looking up.

"Knowing how well my father liked me, I was heartbroken by his reaction when I showed him what I had found. I remember his look of abject horror as if he had seen the vilest apparition; then with barely uncontrollable rage shouted,

"Hand it to me boy. Don't ever speak about what you've found to anyone, not your mother or even your sisters, let alone any of the servants. Promise me that you'll never ever say anything about this discovery to anyone in the future".

"Trembling with fear amidst floods of tears I said that I would never divulge what I had found to anyone".

1795

William Vavour picked his way through the mass of eager shoppers thronging the market stalls in Hoult's High Street. Finding an archway set between two shops he passed through it into Gadfly Passage. By way of contrast to the busy High Street, the passage was quite narrow making it incapable of taking anything a deal wider than a handcart. Over the years the alley had become a convenient dumping ground for rotting vegetables and other rubbish left over from the market stalls. The feeling of gloom and decay was compounded by buildings crowding in on either side.

The raucous sound of the street traders faded to a dull buzz as William looked for a door leading to the office of Ingelby and Good, Solicitors at Law. After a while he discovered the peeling, brown letters of their name painted on a grubby, brown door.

William's eyes had difficulty adjusting to the internal gloom when he noticed a staircase leading to an upper floor.

At its head another door opened onto a room, lit by a solitary north facing window. Eight, tiny, grime encrusted panes overlooked the plain brick wall of the next door building.

The room, apart from being equally as gloomy as the downstairs hallway, had a musty smell about it, which may have originated from the rows of leather bound books that William could see lining the rear wall shelves.

Although the room was spartanly furnished, he didn't immediately notice the hunched figure of a middle aged man perched on a high backed chair to the rear of an even higher desk.

"Mr Ingelby" William said without preamble, presuming that he must be the senior partner and therefore likely to be Ingelby. "Your name was recommended as being someone who could possibly assist me".

Ingelby peered over a pair of round pebble glasses hovering ponderously on the end of his beak like nose. Perhaps as a consequence of working in such an austere environment he frequently had to remove a handkerchief, tucked into the sleeve of his black jacket, to dab a dewdrop on his nose.

"I will do my best to assist you", David Ingelby said, inclining his head in a conspiratorial manner.

"I am William Vavour, and I have a proposition to put business your way".

Ingelby gave a thin smile, as a dew drop fell from his nose onto the pile of documents lining his desk.

"Would this have anything to do with the property that you recently acquired from Jeremy d'Enscout"?

Ignoring the question, William said "I want the cottager who lives next to the entrance to the Park evicted".

"That may be difficult to achieve", Ingelby pronounced, his mind buzzing with ideas on how he could protract the work in order to enhance his fee. "The d'Enscouts you know have been clients of ours for many years. Jeremy's ancestors were responsible for building the manor house and erecting the fine Norman church".

"That's in the past, I own the property now", William declared, drawing his coat a little tighter around his neck in a vain effort to combat the cold draught stealing under the ill fitting door.

"I was sorry to learn of Jeremys' misfortune. I gather he made a poor judgement". Ingelby said, with a shake of his head.

"He was too greedy", William replied.

"Jeremy told me about the enterprise in South America, and how he had been assured that by purchasing shares in the company it would be the soundest investment he ever made".

"Well I told him that there was a slight risk, but he wouldn't listen when he saw his original investment double in value".

"Didn't you warn him it was a highly speculative venture"? Ingelby asked.

"When he saw his investment double again he beseeched me to purchase even more shares for him, but as he had no more money the fool borrowed from me, using the value of his estate as security".

"But the shares started to drop in value" Ingelby pronounced, taking his handkerchief to his nose once more.

"It was like blowing up a pig's bladder", William said with a confident smirk on his face. "Whilst it's soft and supple it will continue to stretch, but once its dry it becomes brittle and is easily burst. Suddenly everyone wanted to sell, causing the price to collapse, and very soon they were worthless".

"Bankrupting Jeremy in the process", Ingelby noted with a thin smile. "Weren't you one of the principle beneficiaries of those share dealings"--- his voice lowered as he shuffled a pile of papers on his desk.

"You traded on your victim's greed to achieve" ---, once again he didn't finish the sentence as he removed his handkerchief from his sleeve, and dabbed his nose once more.

"Like I said, the fool was too greedy, but now I own the estate, I want those peasants with their filthy hovel, cleared off the land. I'm remodelling the old manor house, so I'm not having any of them within sight of the new Hall".

"For perhaps the last four hundred years, the d'Enscouts and cottagers have happily coexisted, why do you want the position to change?".

"They live next to the Park. I've spent good money putting up a pair of iron gates so I don't want the view spoiled by their untidy hovels".

"Remember, their cottager's plots have been handed down from generation to generation, so it's unlikely they'll have any written title to their land. In any case, few, if any, can read or write, so they generally rely on the parson or a benevolent estate owner to guide them through any paperwork".

"That's the reason I'm employing you to get them off. I think you'll know how to confuse them with legal jargon".

"I gather you wish me to produce a document to show the cottagers plot really belongs to the estate, and that they are trespassing by remaining on your land".

"You will be well rewarded provided you carry out my instructions", William said, getting up to leave.

Bill Slade's mud and stud house, with its unkempt thatch roof, looked rather like an ugly wart on the landscape. The couple of rooms that the family lived in shared the same roof as his farm animals.

The untidy appearance of the low dwelling wasn't helped by a heap of rotting manure outside the end of the building where the animals were kept. Nevertheless it was the happy home for his wife Sarah and their five children.

Bill Slade, like his father before him, and son Tom, belonged to a long line of Slades who were born in the village and eked out a living from their small cottager's plot of land down Peddars Lane.

One afternoon in late October as the sun dipped behind an Oak, putting part of the house in shadow, a sprightly horse, pulling a high wheeled gig, turned into the rutted farm entrance.

A thin faced man in a black, high collared coat and matching top hat laid down the reins and slowly stepped from the gig.

"Are you Bill Slade"? He enquired.

Bill and the visitor were quickly surrounded by a gaggle of curious children as his wife appeared in the doorway to see what was happening. Tom the oldest boy moved to the front beside his father. The children's thin faces gave them a lean hungry look which was accentuated by their motley collection of tattered garments. None of the children wore anything on their feet, and even Bill's rough clogs looked incongruous against the fine black buckled shoes of the visitor. David Ingelby sniffed as he extracted a fine lace edged handkerchief from his sleeve and held it to his nose.

He watched half a dozen chickens idly scratching around the edge of the manure heap, as he elaborately unfurled an official looking document and began to read.

"I am instructed by Mr William Vavour to tell you that you are trespassing on his land. Consequently you must leave with all your possessions by sundown tomorrow. If anything is left after that time it will be burnt".

"This is our place. My father was here before me and his father before him. It's always been in our family", Bill said. "He can't turn us off our land".

"I have the documents here to prove this land belongs to the estate. Mr Vavour is merely claiming what is his, now he wants you off his land".

"This is our place", Bill repeated, with barely suppressed anger. "In any case we've nowhere to go".

"Mr Vavours not an unreasonable man, from the goodness of his heart he says you can live in the old woodman's cottage provided you work for him and care for his swine".

"It's a ruin.! No one's lived there as long as I can remember. In any case the roof timbers have collapsed and what's left of the thatch is rotten. We can't live there".

"You need to be thankful he's offered you that. He's no obligation to offer you anything"

"What if we refuse to leave", Bill said.

"Then Mr Vavour will have you arrested for theft of his land. The penalty for theft is imprisonment or deportation".

With that, Ingelby clambered back into the gig and without a backward glance wheeled the pony's head about and set off back to Hoult.

Sarah saw the look of utter despair on her husband's face, but knew only too well how ruthless the ruling classes could be, she remembered how her own father had been treated when he was spotted taking a rabbit from a neighbouring estate.

The younger children began to wail, as Tom with tears running down his face implored his father, "We don't have to leave, do we"?

"I'm afraid there's nothing we can do", Bill said, "Mr Vavours the new owner and he's able to do whatever he wants".

"Is that the reason you take off your cap and bow and we have to curtsey whenever the carriage from the Hall goes by?" Jenny their oldest daughter said.

"It's a mark of respect to our superiors", Sarah replied. "It's a bit like a wide river where we can see them on the other side, but we've no way of crossing it and joining them".

"It's so unfair", Jenny cried, "Isn't there anyone can help us? What about Parson Blades, he's always telling us at Sunday School about fairness and how we should love our neighbours".

"I don't think he'll take our side when he spends so much time at the Hall", Bill replied.

The following day after passing their few livestock to another cottager, Bill, assisted by Tom, loaded their few possessions on a hand cart and moved down to the ruined cottage.

That night the sky glowed as their old home was torched, and the ground levelled as though their cottage had never existed.

Over the course of the next few days Bill was able to make one end of the ruined woodman's cottage habitable. He salvaged the best of the rotting roof timbers and covered them with reeds that he scythed from a nearby ditch. After a day's hard work, tending Mr Vavours pigs, he set about clearing the garden of weeds, in order that he could grow food to feed his family.

Meanwhile, William Vavour set about reconstructing the Manor house transforming it into a stately Hall. He added another floor to the two that were already there and erected a magnificent Georgian facade with symmetrical windows on either side of an elegant front door.

Bill Slade however was not the only cottager to have his property confiscated by the corrupt lawyer producing falsified deeds of ownership.

Neighbours who had lived for generations on their own small plots with access to the common fields, in the adjoining villages where the Vavours owned land, were unceremoniously evicted from their property.

By using the simple expedient of producing an official looking document where none previously existed, was able William Vavour was able to appropriate even larger farms, whilst appearing benevolent to the previous owners by declaring that they could continue to farm the land as one of his tenants paying him a rent. Within five years of acquiring the estate he more than doubled its area.

1815

"I'm cold, wet, and bloody hungry". The young soldier complained.

"Blame Henry Vavour" Tom said, backing further under the hedge to find shelter from the incessant rain.

"Who's e"?

"He's supposed to be looking after our platoon, but spends most of his time with the other officers".

"Was it im what called us filthy peasants"?

"It was, I've known the arrogant devil ever since his father got the estate from Mr d`Enscout".

"Yer don't sound as though you think much on im".

"I've every reason not to; his crooked father tricked us out of our land".

"Why are you `ere then"?

"There wasn't a deal of choice. He told me I had to join the estates platoon, or find out what life was like on a prison ship. I asked him who would care for my wife and bains. Be there in the morning, was all he said. Megs a sensible lass and she`ll do her best for the kids but I'm still worried sick how she'll cope. I knew I had to do as he said, otherwise I might never see them again.

Since leaving the ship a week ago, Tom reckoned it had hardly stopped raining, no wonder the young soldier felt miserable. Even so, he thought that after a life spent in the open air, he was coping better than many of the town men in the company his estate platoon was attached to.

By the subtle use of veiled threats and bribes, William Vavour saw to it that his only son Henry was appointed a captain in charge of the local company that included Tom's platoon.

On his ninth birthday, soon after his father started to care for the estates pigs, Tom started work. From first light until dusk, whatever the weather his task was to prevent crows devouring the freshly sown crops. As he became stronger he helped his father with the pigs, followed a few years later by being detailed to take charge of a team of horses.

Tom had grown into a fine young man inheriting his parent's ethics of decency and fairness; consequently like them he was universally liked. Everyone regarded Meg, the daughter of cottagers from the next parish as being a fitting wife for him. She was sensible where money was concerned, and was exceptionally hard working.

But now, along with the young soldier he was many miles from home and facing the unknown.

"Tomorrow we're going to inflict a devastating defeat on Napoleon's army". Henry stated, viewing the 120 men under his command from the saddle of his stallion. Hold your fire until you see me drop my sword, then commence firing. We want them to fire their muskets first, then we'll have the advantage whilst they concentrate on reloading".

Thump. Thump. Thump. The rhythmical sound from somewhere ahead of them, was intimidating.

"What the 'ells that", the young soldier said.

"It's the drums they're marching to".

"They're scaring the shit out of me".

Conscience Hill